PREDICTIVE MOL___
REDUCING EMERGENCY
DEPARTMENT WAIT TIMES:
A DESCRIPTIVE ANALYSIS OF PATIENT
OVERCROWDING IN PUBLIC HOSPITALS
OF DETROIT, MICHIGAN

Dr. Eric Dewight Williams

PREDICTIVE MODELING REDUCING EMERGENCY DEPARTMENT WAIT TIMES: A
DESCRIPTIVE ANALYSIS OF PATIENT OVERCROWDING IN PUBLIC HOSPITALS OF
DETROIT, MICHIGAN

by

DR. Mountasser Kadrie, Dissertation Chair

Dr. Margaret Carter, Dissertation Committee Member

Dr. Clishia Taylor, Dissertation Committee Member

Dr. David Braga, DBA Program Chair

A Dissertation Presented in Partial Fulfillment

of the Requirements for the Degree of

Doctor of Business Administration

The National Graduate School of Quality Management

January 2016

The National Graduate School of Quality Management

Doctor of Business Administration Committee

Hereby approves the dissertation of

Dr. Eric D. Williams, for the

Degree of Doctor of Business

Administration 2016

Approval Committee:

Dr. Margaret Carter, Chairperson

Dr. Clishia Taylor, Committee Member

Dr. David Braga, Committee Member

Accepted by:

Dr. Eileen Crowley Sullivan,

Dean, Academic Affairs

Charleston, SC
www.PalmettoPublishing.com

PREDICTIVE MODELING REDUCING EMERGENCY DEPARTMENT WAIT TIMES:
A DESCRIPTIVE ANALYSIS OF PATIENT OVERCROWDING IN PUBLIC HOSPITALS OF DETROIT, MICHIGAN
Copyright © 2022 by Dr. Eric Dewight Williams

First Edition

Hardcover:979-8-8229-0616-7
Paperback:979-8-8229-0617-4

Abstract

This dissertation seeks to examine the interactions between staff and patients in the emergency department (ED) waiting room. The manner in which ED waiting rooms are affected by high patient occupancy and low patient flow will be investigated. The demand for emergency care sees a steady increase, and overcrowding causes long wait times, which, in turn, result in dissatisfied patients and high levels of stress in both the staff and patients. Compromised care may occur due to this ED waiting room environment. Reducing wait times may aid in preventing compromised care. The variables affecting both general and more specific issues that arise in relation to long wait times in the ED are addressed. This observational study includes surveys, phone interviews, and face-to-face interactions. Firsthand accounts will be recorded and statistical information will be collected in order to provide a thorough examination on the topic. The first chapter is a standard introduction, providing information about the problem, purpose, and questions related to the study. Chapter 2 provides a literature review of others' work that is helpful in informing this dissertation. Chapter 3 outlines and describes the methodology employed in conducting this study. Chapter 4 presents and analyzes the results of the data collected in this specific work, while chapter 5 explores how this dissertation has contributed to the field. A discussion regarding the implications of this study is included here.

Recommendations for moving forward in light of this new research are provided. The final chapter provides an overall summary of the work done to account for the outcomes and ways to promote future research in this area.

Keywords: emergency department, patient overcrowding, reduced waiting times,

Acknowledgments

This study was accomplished with the support of several persons. The most important thing to acknowledge is our Lord and Savior who has made it possible for all our dreams to become reality. I would like to express my sincere thanks to my good friend Cathy Dockery, who from the very beginning encouraged me to always work hard and continues to be a wonderful mentor on a daily basis. Her guidance and practical advice have pushed me to continuously reconsider my arguments and improve my critical thinking skills. I am forever grateful for her commitment to improving my work ethic and my thinking. I would also like to thank my lovely wife, Monique Williams for her love and continuous support over the years. I express my gratitude to the National Graduate School of Quality Management and its entire staff for their guidance, continuous support, and commitment to the student in providing a quality education. I would like to also acknowledge the Detroit Medical Center and all of its committee members for allowing me to develop this research, and to the employees that work diligently to provide excellent patient care. I would like to acknowledge the ED patients who have provided me with their time, and a deeper understanding that patients do have a voice. Finally, my thankfulness extends to Arlington 1013 DBA classmates, and friends too numerous to mention. I acknowledge their support and want to thank them for their commitment to this program despite the many challenges that we faced. I am grateful, and we will forever be a team despite the long distances between us.

Table of Contents

CHAPTER 1
Introduction

Long waiting times in emergency departments (EDs) have an inverse relationship with the health of patients experiencing acute symptoms of illnesses or severe injuries that warrant medical attention. The composition of ED waiting rooms can help explain numerous demographic definitions. However, hospitals in densely populated urban areas experience significantly longer ED waiting times while large EDs experience longer waiting times. One major issue affecting the overcrowding of EDs within the US healthcare system includes a lack of accessible and affordable primary care facilities. Only a small fraction of US medical doctors practice emergency medicine though most of the patients they serve do not have a comprehensive health care package as they demonstrate need for primary care services.

When applied properly, quality management tools in healthcare settings have positive results in solving the problem of ED overcrowding, leaving room to explore whether these tools can decrease waiting times. However, some limitations exist in that the complex requirements asked of ED staff preclude their ability to apply quality control measures thoroughly. Some studies indicate success though the results are admittedly not generalizable to all populations.

The success of quality management within the ED may rely on top-down leadership focused on structural changes instead of process-based changes. Such structural changes may include improved drug organization and tracking mechanisms, a more standardized charting process, physical reorganization of ED stations, and a focus on solving the bottleneck for patients in triage.

Background and Rationale of the Study

For over 25 years, ED overcrowding was a major focus of research in the medical community in noting a correlation between this problem and derogatory health outcomes (Bernstein et al., 2009). One of the earliest studies published during this time period identified the growing trend of ED overcrowding as a common occurrence instead of an isolated event due to outbreaks of communicable diseases, natural disasters, or incidents with a large number of casualties (Dickinson, 1989). As the literature on ED overcrowding grows, so does the variety of causal links.

A more recent study identified causal links to ED overcrowding by developing a conceptual framework that identified input measures such as non-urgent primary care-seeking patients and "frequent flyer" patients (Hoot & Aronsky, 2008). The study also identified causal links for ED overcrowding in throughput measures such as inadequate ED staffing, and in output measures such as hospital bed shortages. Based on the research conducted over the last 25 years, ED overcrowding reflects a much broader set of inefficient processes within the health care system of the United States.

Statement of the Problem

The negative health outcomes that result from ED overcrowding have ample presence in the research literature.   As a result, a number of strategies and models were developed to identify the causes of this problem. Despite the research that drew attention to identifying the causes of ED overcrowding, the problem remains (Skorga & Young, 2013). Many ED patients find it easy to accept the option of receiving outpatient primary care by nurses and physicians present of how some of them lack any form of health insurance (Skorga & Young, 2013). Public hospitals in the city of Detroit, Michigan, experience lengthy ED wait times. More recently, economic decline in Detroit produced an environment in which low-income patients with little to no health insurance coverage utilize an ED as a source for receiving primary care.

Consequently, an assessment using mixed methods research drawing from both quantitative and qualitative approaches is necessary to analyze the quality of primary care facilities in Detroit's

public hospitals. Mixed methods research attempts to find solutions for patient overcrowding by noting how ED wait times help provide an understanding of how hospitals and patients exercise any and all available options for administering and receiving care.

Purpose of the Study

The purpose of this study is to draw correlations between ED overcrowding, patient wait times, and access to primary health care services within public hospitals located in Detroit, Michigan. The study makes use of quantitative observational data and qualitative reasoning gathered from public hospitals in Detroit. While ED overcrowding is a phenomenon that affects nearly every metropolitan area in the US and worldwide, the exact causes have a wide variation. Overall, the goal of this study is to analyze the current state of ED overcrowding in Detroit and correlate overcrowding with patient wait times and the availability of primary care services.

Research Questions

The primary research questions that inform this study have an overarching goal of exploring the relationship between ED overcrowding and poor health outcomes. In light of recent economic troubles in the Detroit metropolitan area, this study will seek to answer these two questions:

1. What is the current state of patient overcrowding in public hospitals of Detroit, Michigan?
2. How does ED overcrowding affect the health outcomes of patients who must wait in excess of six hours to receive care?

Nature of the Study

This study uses of a mixed methods research model that draws information from Detroit area hospitals in conjunction with data regarding the accessibility of primary health care in exploring the relationships between ED overcrowding, waiting times, and health outcomes. The

primary focus of this research study is on qualitative reasoning, though the study uses quantitative measures to determine the extent of relationships between ED overcrowding, patient wait times, and poor health outcomes. Qualitative reasoning provides a textual description of the effects that ED overcrowding and longer wait times has on the health outcomes of low income citizens within the Detroit metropolitan area. A mixed methods approach will not attempt to show causation between these variables, and will not involve manipulating the variables. This study involved a systematic process of data collection to define and describe the state of health care in the Detroit metropolitan area. Correlations between variables in this study led to an analysis of explanations to develop a broad understanding of ED overcrowding in public hospitals of Detroit.

Definition of Terms

Emergency Department (ED)

An ED is a medical facility that emphasizes the treatment of acute medical or trauma- related emergencies. The ED typically has a central location within a hospital environment or other health care facility, and patients have the freedom to arrive independently or through the utilization of an emergency medical service such as an ambulance (Delgado et al., 2013; Schull et al., 2003). All conditions, regardless of severity, gain admission into the facility for treatment or diversion to specialized facilities (Afilalo et al., 2004; Dent et al., 2003; Durand et al., 2012; Gentile et al., 2010; Liaw et al., 2014; Pitts et al., 2010; Russ et al., 2008; Schull et al., 2007).

The broad ranges of issues that patients present within an ED require medical personnel with a broad range of medical expertise.

Patient Flow

This term refers to the movement of patients into and out of an ED, and has similarities with product streams in industrial production facilities (Bair, Song, Chen, & Morris, 2010;

Cheng et al., 2013). The specifics of patient flow into and out of an ED differ in many ways (Bair et al., 2010; Becker & Friedman, 2013; Bernstein et al., 2003; Finn et al., 2013; Liu et al., 2013; McCarthy et al., 2011; McClelland et al., 2011). Patient overcrowding prior to entrance into an ED has a relationship with issues in downstream patient flow. Some of these issues include low admittance availability, low staffing, and case complexity (Dickinson, 1989; Hoot & Aronsky, 2008; Lin, Patrick, & Labeau, 2014). ED overcrowding prevents timely access to care as delays in treatment may worsen the severity of symptoms in some patients.

Customer Voice

In the US healthcare system, the staff who work in an ED have an obligation to treat acute emergencies to the best of their ability. Customer voice is a representation of this duty as the situations ED patients present in preclude a true ability to express their personal rights. Put differently, customer voice is a tool for patients to express their satisfaction or dissatisfaction with the level of health care they received in an ED (Jennings et al., 2015; Messina et al., 2015; Obamiro, 2013). This research area in studies of ED crowding is relatively new. However, factors such as the role of nurse practitioner (Jennings et al., 2015), receiving information about waiting times and delays on a regular basis (Messina et al., 2015), and receiving health care services after an appropriate amount of time (Obamiro, 2013) have effects on patient satisfaction.

Overcrowding

The influx of patients has a correlation with patient flow. Effects of patient flow may have a correlation with downstream issues such as low admittance availability, low staffing, and case complexity. Overcrowding in this context has a direct correlation with increased ED patient wait times. An implicit assumption here is that patient overcrowding has inversely proportional relationship to patient health outcomes. In some cases, patients in an ED with more severe symptoms may need to wait longer than those who have less severe symptoms but arrive later.

Patients with mental illness may also need to wait longer than other patients in an ED regardless of overcrowding (Atzema et al., 2012). Overcrowding significantly and negatively affects the domains of quality care as identified by the Institute of Medicine (IOM): safety, patient-centered care, timeliness, efficiency, effectiveness, and equity (Bernstein et al., 2009). While previous arguments about ED overcrowding involved the frequency of ambulance diversion to other hospitals, the standards used to measure overcrowding have a low reliability rate (McCarthy et al., 2011). Current measurements for ED overcrowding control for the number of arrivals (input), the number of patients treated (throughput), and waiting/boarding time (output). Some measures for assessing the problem of ED overcrowding further involve the use of models such as the Emergency Department Work Index (EDWIN) or the National Emergency Department Overcrowding Scale (NEDOCS), though these models often yield similar conclusions regarding the effects of ED overcrowding on health outcomes (McCarthy et al., 2011). Nevertheless, some measures of overcrowding have a higher level effectiveness for routine use based on the organizational environment of an ED.

Waiting Time

This term refers to the amount of time spent in a pre-care situation prior to admission into an ED. Boarding time is another way of defining waiting time in an ED (Ding et al., 2010). An expanded definition provided by Ding and colleagues (2010) asserts that waiting time includes a total of completion time by patient, clinical, crowding, and time-related factors for receiving different levels of quality in emergency care. The quality of service completion times as patients wait to receive care vary across each different type of ED (Ding et al., 2010). Locating the barriers for patients to receive quality health care in an ED will involve developing accurate models of waiting times.

Synergy Effect

This term includes the effect on patient flow because of increased communication between working units and efforts to decrease waste. Facility management has critical importance for helping ED staff handle negative economic impacts and increase performance capacity (Hajduková & Figuli, 2013). The synergy effect of an ED involves having to consider overhead costs within the context of professional administration and support processes for business management (Hajduková & Figuli, 2013). Facilities management may include considerations of benefits associated with more efficient and effective responses to market demands, outsourcing activities to different departments, professionalism, use of best practices, rapid transfers of knowledge, and accurate predictions of cost and cost-effectiveness (Hajduková & Figuli, 2013). While managing for cost remains important for any ED, maintaining the function of an ED while accounting for value necessitates the need for staff to reconsider strategies for improving capacity and decreasing waiting times for patients.

Mixed Methods Research.

As noted in Chapter III, the popularity of mixed methods research in the social sciences extends to the health sciences. The application of research findings, theoretical frameworks, and anecdotes across a variety of platforms and subjects draws from mixed methods to focus research questions on one specific variable or field of study. Mixed methods research has multiple definitions presented in the literature of multiple disciplines, though most definitions emphasize the following approaches: a focus on the development of research questions emphasizing a "real- life contextual understanding," multiple perspectives, cultural influences; the use of quantitative research methods to assess the magnitude and frequency of theoretical constructs; the use of qualitative research methods to explore the meaning and understanding of theoretical constructs; the use of multiple methods, such as intervention trials and in-depth interviews; an intentional integration or triangulation of methods that draw on their individual strength; and developing an

investigative framework for arguing philosophical and theoretical positions (Creswell et al., 2011, p. 4). Mixed methods research often has a diverse set of philosophical and theoretical positions that bridge a gap between the strict use of empirical data and arguments that all research concepts are social constructions. At the same time, mixed methods research highlights the use of pragmatist and transformative perspectives that emphasize developing a theory of practice for restructuring how some institutions function (Creswell, et al., 2011). Overall, mixed methods research in the health sciences presents opportunities to develop new knowledge by finding common ground between seemingly disparate theoretical and philosophical positions.

Variables

Individual units of interest within a research consideration. Variables may be present or absent, changing or immoveable, authentic or inferred.

Acuteness

As a measure of objective timeliness, in which the presence of some activity or state is of immediate concern, acuteness refers to medical or trauma-related emergencies within patients in an ED. Some hospital staff decide to use discretion when determining what constitutes an acute condition that warrants a lesser waiting time than other patients (Kellerman & Weinick, 2012).

Patients who often rely on an ED as a source of primary care may not necessarily have acute symptoms of a health condition nor do they necessarily have a severe injury. Arguably, these patients are a cause of ED overcrowding (Liaw et al., 2014). However, with respect to health outcomes, if some patients wait in an ED for too long, the likelihood of mortality is greater.

Performance Measurements

Within the research on patient overcrowding, performance measurements refer to the scales and grades of output by working units within an ED, independent or dependent on patient flow. Some research findings from previous studies support a wide range of interventions for

improving both patient satisfaction and health outcomes (Boudreaux, Cruz, & Baumann, 2006).

Complaints by patients about the service they receive while waiting in an ED influence the need for increased involvement from hospital staff to improve efficiency and effectiveness (Griffey & Bohan, 2006). Performance measurements often refer to controlling for quality of care and improving organizational efficiency.

Plan-Do-Study-Act (PDSA) Process.

This process has implications for implementing quality management tools as they relate to healthcare systems. Some quality management tools may involve re-drawing the physical design of an ED by emphasizing the domains of space, equipment, and patient accessibility (Majidi et al., 2014). Moreover, some departments have a lower patient capacity than other departments (Jaeker, Tucker, & Lee, 2013). One way of improving patient flow is to apply queueing theory in designing a structure for benchmarking ideal wait times (Lin et al., 2014). Queueing theory typically models two different threads—one of which involves the time patients arrive at an ED until they leave and the other of which involves a general arrival process with independently distributed service times among patients waiting to receive care (Lin et al., 2014). Models that apply queueing theory represent a steady stream of access to care while waiting in an ED.

Staff Resistance

Staff resistance is a result of complex requirements already placed on ED staff. Resistance to changes in quality management includes infrastructure, leadership, and organizational culture (Hudson et al., 2014). Infrastructural barriers include a lack of engagement among ED personnel in data collection, information technology (IT) specialists working outside of an ED, lack of funding for projects to improve quality, and lack of communication between IT and ED personnel (Hudson et al., 2014). Leadership barriers include

the inability to participate directly in projects to improve quality while barriers related to organizational culture refer more to overall resistance to change (Hudson et al., 2014). The organizational culture of an ED may also undergo frequent changes while the internal environment involves ED staff caring for patients with little time to have involvement in projects to improve quality.

Service Quality

The measurement of ED perception by patients that encompasses waiting time, treatment, level of care, and subjective standards of expectation. In some EDs, increasing capacity may actually increase wait times (Jaeker, Tucker, & Lee, 2013). Service quality depends on the availability of resources more than it depends on increasing capacity. Not only can increasing ED capacity also increase wait times, it may also lead to a decrease in service quality (Jaeker et al., 2013). Yet despite a lessening of service quality in some EDs that increase patient capacity, the likelihood of mortality decreases (Crilly et al., 2014). These observations led to the suggestion that because EDs have an important role to play within an entire health care delivery system, future research will need to consider how service quality depends on a combination of available resources and capacity levels.

Significance of Study

The growing trend of increased ED waiting times in economically developed countries has detrimental consequences to both patients and healthcare systems. Unfortunately, researchers have yet to reach a clear consensus on the proper mechanisms that should apply to reducing ED wait times in hospitals throughout the United States. ED overcrowding leads to low hospital rankings regarding the quality of care that patients receive (ACEP Medical Legal Committee, 2013). The state of Michigan received one of the lowest ratings for quality of services in an ED, ranking forty-sixth out of fifty (Hirshon et al., 2013). The National Quality

Forum, a US-based medical forum, pairs yearly rates of patients who leave an ED without being seen with the length of stay (LOS) in an ED to consider a true measure of quality and efficiency (Carron et al., 2014; Guttman, Schull, Vermeulen, & Sturkel, 2011; Lovett et al., 2014).

However, gaps in knowledge are apparent in those measures. Thus, the significance of this study is in its focus on identifying quality management tools that reduce waiting times to a maximum target of four hours and improve the quality of care patients receive while waiting in an ED at a public hospital in Detroit.

Defining the types of quality management tools that ED staff should implement reflects a growing need to understand the current state of ED overcrowding in hospitals. Only four percent of US doctors comprise the work force in EDs though they handle approximately 28 percent of acute care cases (Hirshon et al., 2014). Confounding this is an 11 percent drop in the number of EDs between 1995 and 2010 in conjunction with a continued trend of increased patient volume seeking primary care services in this area (Hirshon et al. 2014). Such a decrease in the number of EDs entails a significant increase in the expectations and workloads for doctors, physicians, and nurses.

The demographics of patients who use an ED as a primary source of care present variables related to overcrowding. In Illinois, for example, hospitals with larger EDs have longer wait times (Wang, 2013). EDs at ten Illinois hospitals with the longest wait times were in some of the largest hospitals of the state. More specifically, most of these hospitals have their location in the Chicago metropolitan area (Wang, 2013, para 12). Conversely, the ten EDs in Illinois hospitals with the shortest waiting times were central to wealthier suburban areas (para. 12).

Based on these results, the average ED waiting time in Illinois hospitals is 260 minutes—or four hours and twenty minutes—slightly below the national average waiting time of 274 minutes, or four hours and thirty-four minutes (para. 14). The results in this context should come as no surprise. Wealthier suburban areas tend to have less dense populations, higher tax revenue streams, and more expensive privately-owned hospitals. As a stark contrast, urban areas like Chicago and Detroit have nearly the exact opposite demographics as suburban areas.

Consequently, hospitals in the Chicago metropolitan cater to public needs have much larger EDs and therefore have patients experiencing longer waiting times.

Some public hospitals in the Chicago metropolitan area—e.g., "safety net" and educational/academic hospitals—had the largest EDs and the longest waiting times (Wang, 2013, para. 2). The university of Chicago Medical Center, the University of Illinois Hospital, the Northwestern Memorial Hospital, and a host of Cook County Health and Hospital System locations posted waiting times of over six and one-half hours (Wang, 2013). While it is easy to understand the economic demographics at play in reading these raw numbers, it appears more difficult to understand why health systems in close proximity can have such widely varying waiting times. Recent debates in the US centered on access to health insurance may speak to the discrepancies seen between suburban and urban areas. Not only is the load of uninsured patients increasing within EDs because of how they sometimes function as a source for primary care, EDs will remain so until these patients receive federally-subsidized insurance. Using the ED as a source of primary care is a common practice in densely populated and largely poor urban areas. For example, the city of Houston, Texas, has the highest proportion of uninsured patients in the US as it also has the highest number of uninsured primary care cases within EDs (Begley, Behan & Seo, 2010). Demographic categories like race, geographic location, and socioeconomic status present underlying factors associated with increased waiting times in EDs while insurance status represents an overarching factor (Begley et al., 2010). The main issue in Houston and nearly all major cities in the US, as indicated by the increased ED waiting times, is a lack of access to primary care facilities.

Quality management within an ED has a strong correlation to a more efficient system of healthcare delivery and a decreased amount of time patients spent waiting for treatment. Quality management, however, is a process that must take place over time with a number of industry- specific considerations. The principles of quality management were first applied to industrial assembly line processes. Thus, its application to ED overcrowding lends itself to the development of a context-based approach (Bair, Song, Chen, & Morris, 2010; Cheng et al., 2013). The ED is a staple of healthcare systems in economically developed countries, with the provision of high quality acute care a seemingly inherent right (Francis, Spies, & Kerner, 2008). The core values of an ED in the US affirm this right by focusing on the goal of creating positive health outcomes in acute cases. Growing evidence supports the need for hospitals to decrease the amount of time patients wait to receive care in an ED.

The complexities of an ED make the identification of specific quality management parameters difficult.

The significance of studies such as this one depends on defining parameters of quality management. Decreasing ED waiting times has benefits to both staff and patients.

However, a process that ensures decreased ED waiting times should not come at the cost of decreasing quality. The strength of applying quality management practices to an ED is threefold. Quality management offers strong and reliable systems of control while it also offers a clerical system for plotting efficient measures. Moreover, quality management measures the allocation of resources that determine the level of service patients receive (Oberklaid et al., 1991). Quality management aims to provide a sound organizational infrastructure as the result of educational training for ED staff, evaluations of health outcomes after receiving care in an ED, and documenting the process of delivering healthcare to determine outcomes for patients.

Identifying the parameters of quality management is a necessary step in an effort to decrease the amount of time-spent waiting in an ED at public hospitals.

Defining the parameters for quality management in an ED cannot occur without a firm understanding of the factors affecting care provision. The general understanding is that as patient volume increases, workload for ED staff—physicians, nurses, physician assistants, technicians, respiratory aids, and other supplementary staff—also increases. However, workloads among hospital staff rarely have an even distribution. Increased workloads among hospital staff potentially increase ED waiting times and negatively affect the health outcomes of patients with acute symptoms of an illness or a severe injury (Oberklaid et al., 1991). Handling a broad array of patients with different types of medical conditions requires the application of a top-down process with a spotlight on efficiency as emerging cases generally decrease productivity. The problem of increased ED waiting times has further complications when inexperienced or junior members are the primary staff, or when experienced staff members already have a burdensome workload (Oberklaid et al., 1991). An ED must remain open at all hours and in all conditions. Any changes in staffing lead to significant changes in the expectations of providing care.

Streamlining the process of ED care may present significant difficulties, though quality management techniques have a noted strength in guiding improvements. In an assessment of changes implemented within an ED, one study made an analogy to the Toyota Production System's Andon Cord (Goralnick, Walls, & Kosowsky, 2013). The Andon Cord is a quality control method used by Toyota automobile manufacturing facilities in Japan to identify problems with production streams so that analysts, managers, and production workers can focus their efforts on solving problems as they emerge (Chan et al., 2014). Team members may recognize the causes of problems, and management can act more efficiently to quell the issue. Prior to implementing Andon Cord-like process to their ED, Goralnick et al. (2013) noted that a reduction of wait time to 65 minutes led to patients rating their satisfaction between the sixth and 40th percentiles. Within five years, they were able to decrease the wait time to 22 minutes, and patient satisfaction rested between the 90th and 99th percentiles despite cutting ED staff by half of what it was previously (Goralnick et al., 2013). Decreasing ED wait times and increasing patient satisfaction involved the identification of key stakeholders in care provision and the imposition of high expectations for success in delivering quality care to patients. Analysts worked with staff subdivided into groups to conduct routine checks, change pathways to service provision, and adopt a strategy of placing any patient in any bed as space permitted (Goralnick et al., 2013).

The Andon Cord in the above example streamlined services at an ED by significantly decreasing waiting times and increasing patient satisfaction. Most likely, an increase in positive health outcomes resulted in the use of an Andon Cord streamlining process.

Similar to the use of an Andon Cord is an application of lean production techniques. Lean production techniques focus on decreasing waste while products "flow smoothly, continuously, and without errors from one step to another" (Holden, 2011, p. 265). Lean production has its roots in the philosophy of lean thinking that emphasizes the elimination of elements that produce little value so that individuals on the receiving end of a production line obtain the highest value possible (Chan et al., 2014). In an ED, patients are the products. Waste elimination in lean thinking has a direct correlation to a maximal value for patients.

One study identified other principles of lean production techniques that have relevance within EDs including a decrease in the production (patient care) stream, decrease in the stock inventories, worker empowerment, immediate identification of problems, solving problems at their source in an effort to decrease multiple similar instances from occurring, and efforts in continuous improvement (Holden, 2011, p. 266). In an ED these factors play different roles; however, providing sufficient details in applications of lean production techniques has important implications for providing quality care. Here, lean management practices entail the recognition and elimination of steps in processes that contribute minimal value to providing services for patients waiting in an ED (Chan et al., 2014). Lean management practices also entail the recognition of processes that waste time and increase ED wait times.

Specific changes to ED processes can include an increased speed of assessments by physicians and nurse by using a more standardized charting technique, eliminating outdated policies or revising current ones, combining steps within the process of care provision, admissions of patients to any area of the hospital that has capacity, and a more standardized medication storage and labeling process. ED systems can also undergo changes. One study found that despite their incredible decrease in ED wait times, the primary bottleneck that maintained any waiting time at all was the initial triage process (Goralnick et al., 2013). The researchers identified a bottleneck by compiling accurate data for benchmarking wait times within units of the E studied. Other considerations for system changes included better educational training as time permitted, improved communication tools, improvements in teamwork throughout departments, and assigning specialists to match peak patient volumes at different times (Holden, 2011). Quality management is an important factor for developing strategic processes to decrease ED waiting times. However, gaps in the application of lean management principles remain. An understanding of risk within the ED is a primary component of proper quality management, and a major factor in decreasing amounts of available resources. Moreover, the process of benchmarking to establish a maximum allowable wait time encourages hospital staff to make improvements wherever possible.

Benchmarking

Benchmarking, or the process of creating comparative analysis between similar organizations or units within an organization, represents an important factor in decreasing the gaps of knowledge as they apply to decreasing the waiting times of ED patients. One study cited the use of disease-specific markers as a valuable measure of effective ED care (Francis et al., 2008). Benchmarks often apply a goal-oriented framework to achieve improvements of quality by reducing errors and streamlining medical procedures. The core values of quality improvements in benchmarking include supervision, interdisciplinary communication, and individual self-control mechanisms (Francis et al., 2008). These core values should remain a top priority for analysts, supervisors, and team members at all times.

A cohort study from Ontario showed why these factors of quality assurance should remain a top priority (Guttmann et al., 2011). Patients with acute symptoms during periods of long waiting times were much more likely to leave without being seen (LWBS), and had an increased risk of death for up to seven days following ED presentation (Guttmann et al., 2011). The increasing burden of primary care provision presents a growing problem. Any shifts in the landscape of a healthcare system will likely produce more gaps in knowledge. Support for programs that facilitate swifter transition to more focused and pertinent care have a likelihood of decreasing waiting times for patients in an ED (Hirshon et al., 2014). Support in this manner entails a political need to lobby for increased primary care facilities linked with EDs or linked to geographic locations that significantly detrimental ED burdens.

A recent study suggested that more time should be devoted to funding disaster preparedness programs, increase investment in information technologies, increase funding for graduate medical education programs that focus specifically on emergency care, and the implementation of better drug monitoring systems (Hirshon et al., 2014). Quality management tools like streamlining patient care, increasing the quality of orientation and educational practices, and focusing resources will more effectively decrease ED waiting times. However, limitations have recognition in how effectively an ED staff manages resources to care for patients with the most acute symptoms as these areas of a hospital may use its capacity to the highest possible limits (Wang, 2013). The significance of studies like this rests in identifying how far the efforts of ED staff may reach by highlighting gaps of knowledge in quality management practices.

Assumptions and Limitations

The assumptions of this study have a wide distribution in the literature previously discussed. Increased ED waiting times throughout hospitals in the US have a detrimental effect on the healthcare system as a whole, though increased waiting times adversely affect individual patient health more significantly. While some scholarly debate drew attention to the applicability of rights and responsibilities of governing bodies to provide high quality emergency care for its citizens at face value, the findings and evidence suggest that healthcare practitioners are tasked with providing the highest quality care possible.

The central assumption of this study is that ED and other hospital staff benefit from decreased ED waiting times. This assumption factors into quality management tools discussed earlier and later on in this study. The streamlining of patient care techniques and processes benefits from a decreased burden throughout an entire healthcare system. A secondary assumption is that quality management tools for decreasing ED waiting times can also apply to the American health care system. This assumption implies that hospitals experiencing ED overcrowding and increased waiting times on a frequent basis have an opportunity to consider strategies made by staff at various hospitals and apply them to specific contexts.

The limitations of this study have parameters defined by a number of geographic, economic, and situational factors. Debates on whether a high number of uninsured citizens has a correlation with lengthy ED waiting times in the US healthcare system reflects changes implemented by reforms in the health insurance industry. These debates may lead to significant developments regarding the practical implications of findings in this study (Begley et al., 2010).

Another limitation is in the application of quality management tools within a healthcare setting. While some studies have findings suggestive of improvements to ED waiting times (Goralnick et al, 2013), sample sizes are often low and claims of improving the quality of care often have a subjective nature.

Scope of the Study

The extent of this study is in identifying trends, factors, and specific measurements of ED overcrowding and excessive wait times. The central hypothesis of this study is that the persistent problem of ED overcrowding and excessive waiting times affects the quality of care received by patients and delivered by ED staff. Quantitative and qualitative measures provide methodological tools for identifying gaps in the research literature devoted to measuring the effects of increased waiting time in EDs throughout the US.

Quantitative measures rely on measurements of overcrowding and lengthy wait time measure for retrospective ED data. Measurements of o provide a better quantification of the effect that ED waiting time have on the health of patients. While ED waiting time affects patient health in a negative way, so too does speedy discharge from the ED (Guttman et al., 2011). A measure of the effect of waiting times on the outcome of a patient's care may speak to gaps in the knowledge of studies like this. Qualitative measures rely heavily on the assumptions stated and explored in past literature. Identification of gaps in knowledge within that literature is an important aspect of defining what qualitative measures have the most significant theoretical and practical implications for health professionals. Whereas quality management strategies have practical implications, they remain largely theoretical in how many ED staff members refuse to accept as changes in practices for improving hospital care.

Theoretical Framework

The primary area of theoretical interest is the quality management of healthcare systems, specifically for EDs within hospitals belonging to the US healthcare system. Specific areas of interest are: the ED waiting room itself, the parameters that influence overcrowding, and the subsequent waiting time for patients experiencing acute health emergencies. An initial assumption about acute emergencies is that a patient health has an inversely proportionate relationship with the amount of time spent waiting to receive medical care. While correlations between increased waiting time and decreased care have a presence in the research literature (Begley et al., 2010), overcrowded EDs in US public hospitals contain patients who require treatments and therapies often used in primary care settings.

The research questions focus on the broad effects of increased waiting room times on healthcare systems specifically within the ED waiting room itself. If increased ED overcrowding and increased ED waiting times negatively affect patient health when experiencing an acute medical emergency, an assumption to make is that the ED as a whole will experience negative consequences. The research questions investigate the problems that arise when such a burden occurs, but they will not focus on the specific properties of the medical emergencies discussed throughout this study. Whether ED staff can effectively implement quality management measures remains unknown, though some studies applied lean production techniques and quality management measures to healthcare settings for decreasing wait times in an ED and improving patient health outcomes (Holden, 2011). Thus, the purpose of this study is to explore the applicability of quality management measures to Eds. Underscoring this purpose is an investigation into whether or not quality management strategies effectively decrease waiting times for patients in an ED to account for satisfaction with services and improved health outcomes.

CHAPTER 2:
Literature Review

ED overcrowding is a major focus in 25 years of published research on healthcare systems in economically developed countries. The US healthcare system is an example of the interplay between private insurance providers, rising healthcare costs, and decreasing standards of health. The obligation to provide high quality care does not always meet the ability to pay for it. Thus, the US government granted some legislative protections over the years. In 1986, the 99th Congressional session enacted the Emergency Medical Treatment & Labor Act (EMTALA) to provide emergency healthcare to anyone in need regardless of legal citizenship status or the ability to pay for healthcare services. Congress passed EMTALA in conjunction with the Consolidated Omnibus Budget Reconciliation Act (COBRA) by mandating that all hospitals who receive federal payments for Medicare-covered services accept all patients who present symptoms of acute traumatic or medical emergencies.

Shortly after Congress passed EMTALA, early studies on ED overcrowding highlighted the difficult situations in which patients and healthcare providers find themselves. One of the earliest studies identified ED overcrowding is inevitable because of the transitory and unscheduled nature of emergencies. As is the case today, incidents of ED overcrowding happened not only as the direct result of isolated events like mass casualty incidents or influenza outbreaks (Dickinson, 1989). In many instances, the number of patients waiting to receive care exceeds the number of available beds during the triage process after arriving by ambulance.

Hence, earlier research suggested that closing an ED to patients arriving by ambulance was a solution to decreasing wait times (Dickinson, 1989). Closing an ED to ambulatory patients may lead to a less congested ED while patients waiting to receive will likely have ED staff assign them to a bed. Unfortunately, closing an ED to ambulatory patients leads to negative health consequences for those experiencing acute symptoms and severe injuries. Ambulance drivers and emergency medical technicians (EMTs) must transfer patients to distant facilities.

Moreover, some EMTs only have enough training to offer basic resuscitative measures. Delaying and rerouting ambulatory services may lead to further complications and/or death.

Because of having to re-route ambulatory patients, ED staff at different hospitals report feelings of frustration. Re-routing ambulatory patients creates further inefficiencies in a health care system. The earlier research noted how an ED facility that operates inefficiently is also one that stretches its resources (Dickinson, 1989). Resource scarcity at a hospital and in an ED implies that staff does not have the authority to simply admit patients, but that staff may need to facilitate early discharges for providing more bed space. Admissions into an ED accounts for approximately half of admissions in most large hospitals, and the number of open beds in an ED should remain plenty. As such, closing an ED to patients arriving by ambulance poses a major crisis in the health care industry. ED overcrowding results in hospitals eventually losing the capacity to handle crises as they emerge (Dickinson, 1989). Arguably, access to an ED must remain open to the public.

Some of the earlier research also observed the detrimental effects of ED overcrowding in public hospitals of New York City (Gallagher & Lynn, 1990). The effects of ED overcrowding are obvious if not easily discernible. Adverse health outcomes such as patient mortality, reduced quality of care, transport delays, impaired access to care such as ambulance diversion and patient elopement, and financial losses incurred by hospitals stand out. What is less obvious, and thus constitutes a primary research focus for most of the medical community over the past few decades, are the factors that bring about adverse health outcomes. From the large breadth of work that has helped researchers develop practical knowledge of how to recognize ED overcrowding, two types of available models help with providing a knowledge basis for this study.

The Input-Throughput-Output model and other Quality Improvement (QI) measures— including Kotter's 8-Step Model, the PRECEED/PROCEED Model, CIPP/Stufflbeam Model, and clinical microsystems—help researchers identify causal links of either positive or negative health outcomes over the course of treating a patient requiring ED services (Hoot & Aronsky, 2008, Liu et al., 2013). At the input level, common problems addressed by researchers include non-urgent or primary care-oriented visits, frequent flyer patients, and influenza season. At the throughput level, common problems include inadequate staffing, and at the output level common problems include inpatient boarding and hospital bed shortages (Hoot & Aronsky, 2008). By identifying problems along a timeline of an ED patient's experience, certain QI measures can be applied to an underperforming ED.

Questions Guiding the Research

Two research questions guide the course of this study. The overarching goal of answering the research questions is to explore the relationship between ED overcrowding and adverse health outcomes. In light of recent economic troubles in the Detroit metropolitan area, this study asks:

1. What is the current state of patient overcrowding at emergency departments of public hospitals in the city of Detroit, Michigan?

2. How does ED overcrowding affect the health outcomes of patients who must wait in excess of six hours to receive care?

Methods for Reviewing Literature

The literature review analyzes research related to patient overcrowding, primary care access within the American health care system, and QI measures within the American health care system. Primary articles are those selected from journals with impact factors of 3.0 or greater.

Impact factors for article selection depended on the extent to which researcher's analyzed patient overcrowding in the context of the Input-Throughput-Output conceptual framework, primary care seeking non-urgent patients, and current trends in QI for patient overcrowding. The primary

database used for literature searches was PubMed. Reviews were selected that met primary source criteria, and pertinent sources were taken for further examination. Inclusion criteria for non-review articles included any study with an ED as its study site that sought to correlate the problem of patient overcrowding with adverse health outcomes. Studies with findings that refuted claims made in these reports were also included.

Method for Analyzing the Literature

Due to the high degree of variability in causes explaining negative health outcomes, journal articles that included specific populations of subjects with a direct one-to-two correlational relationship to patient overcrowding in an ED were useful for assessing the research literature. A one-to-two correlational relationship between ED overcrowding and the following subjects—access to primary care, non-urgent ED utilization, clinical outcomes, quality improvement (QI) strategies, and health insurance—were explored. The literature that resulted from this selection process was then analyzed for timeliness, applicability to research objectives, and applicability to arguments found in primary sources. The primary focus during this analysis was reliability in terms of consistency, repeatability, and validity. Best practices to date received some attention during the process of reviewing the published scholarly literature. However, significant differences between the causal factors of patient overcrowding assessed in this study could not result in a full consensus regarding which sources to include. The primary disadvantage of the current research methodology found in this analysis was the lack of published data across a broad spectrum of geographic locations and demographic backgrounds.

Inner-city public hospitals, for example, have more substantive problems associated with patient overcrowding as poorer patients lack health insurance compared to patients at suburban public hospitals. Yet, despite how socioeconomic stratification exists on a number of different levels, it does not always act as a causal factor of patient overcrowding in an ED.

Selected Processes

A number of models were used to address different aspects of this study. While the primary theme is ED overcrowding, secondary themes took on different characteristics. In terms of QI, research articles drew insights from the disciplines of business management, human resources, and supply chain management (SCM). Demographic studies provided data obtained through ethnography and participant observation whereas clinical studies provided results from empirical studies. Studies that included public health surveys also helped in identifying correlations between themes and models. All of the studies used in this literature review were selected and included in this study based on the identification of relationships between two or more variables related to patient overcrowding. Though conclusions about causal relations could have included an unmeasured variable, definitive causal conclusions between increased ED waiting times and adverse health outcomes for patients are not possible to make.

Organization of Studies According to Theme

Studies with a direct one-to-two correlational relationship to patient overcrowding in ED's were used to analyze database results from PubMed. Articles that fit the previously described parameters were included in the literature review. The accepted studies were organized according to the following themes: causes of patient overcrowding, infrequent events, access to primary care facilities, clinical health outcomes, QI and QI strategies, and financial implications.

Synthesis

The primary causes of ED overcrowding are well documented, yet they remain varied and misunderstood. The problem of ED overcrowding remains as deleterious today as it was when the problem first gained attention in the United States over 25 years ago. The reasons as to why waiting rooms in an ED become overcrowded are remarkable. Events like influenza

outbreaks and natural disasters have the ability to create temporary influxes of demand for healthcare services (Glaser et al., 2002; Russo, 2006). An ED may have problems associated with an inadequate amount of fully trained staff. Hospitals can also experience problems like bed shortages and problems with in-patient admissions.

The most pressing issue is that of access to primary health care after the recent economic recession. Access to primary health care sparked a continued national debate on access to affordable health insurance coverage based on legislative measures enacted at the federal level. The intended consequences of those legislative changes remain unknown. However, hospitals across the United States are currently in the process of developing QI measures to reduce patient overcrowding. QI measures such as identification platforms, mobile admissions devices, and real-time collaborations have helped decrease patient overcrowding in certain regions.

Unfortunately, the problem persists as one of the most important issues for the American health care system.

Discussion

The root causes, metrics for identification, and consequences of ED overcrowding are well documented, yet the problem remains as detrimental to the health outcomes of patients as it does to an entire healthcare system. The literature review addresses the main causes of ED overcrowding with an emphasis on non-urgent patients presenting only minor symptoms of illness or injury to ED staff. The literature review also investigates alternative causes to patient overcrowding in an ED and its effect on the health outcomes of patients. Alternative causes of patient overcrowding include inadequate or improper ED staffing, in-patient admissions, and hospital bed shortages. These causes often result in negative health outcomes for admitted patients. Thus, the strategies used to predict, control, and reduce ED overcrowding are important to this literature review. While ED staff at a large number of hospitals have tried to implement

numerous interventions to reduce overcrowding. Evidence from the research literature suggests that more informed QI measures must coincide with legislative changes in order to increase the efficiency of EDs, decrease unnecessary ED utilization by non-urgent patients, improve the quality of care receive, and improve the health outcomes of patients in need of emergency care.

Causes of Patient Overcrowding in an ED

Patient overcrowding has multiple, though not always related, causes. Hoot and Aronsky (2008) developed a conceptual framework for studying the causes of patient overcrowding in an ED with a focus on input, throughput, and output measures. Input factors reflect the sources and aspects of patient inflow while throughput factors reflect bottlenecks within an ED and output factors reflect bottlenecks in other parts of the health care system that might effect and ED (Hoot & Aronsky, 2008). Patient overcrowding represents an international crisis that affects the quality of and access to health care (Hoot & Aronsky, 2008). Common causes of overcrowding include non-urgent visits, "frequent flyer" patients (Dent et al., 2003), influenza outbreaks (Glaser et al., 2002; Russo, 2006), inadequate staffing, inpatient boarding (Singer, Thode, Viccellio, & Pines, 2011), and hospital bed shortages (Blom, Jonsson, Landin-Olsson, & Guttman et al., 2011; Hoot & Aronsky, 2008; Ivarsson, 2014).

The effects of overcrowding, in turn, include patient mortality (Bernstein et al., 2009), transport delays, treatment delays, ambulance diversion (Dickinson, 1989), destination control, crowding measures, and queueing theory (Hoot & Aronsky, 2008; Lin et al., 2014). Input measures include non-urgent visits, frequent flyer patients, and influenza outbreaks. Inadequate staffing is a throughput factor while inpatient boarding and hospital bed shortages are output factors (Hoot & Aronsky, 2008). Solutions for patient overcrowding included the hiring of more ED staff, the inclusion of more observation units, increased access to hospital beds, and referrals for non-urgent patients.

Hoot and Aronsky (2008) suggested that applications of queueing theory may provide management tools for standard operations to improve ED patient flow. The airline and manufacturing industries have already applied queueing theory by promoting an organizational system with various inputs and a fixed capacity will only remain congested or overcrowded for short periods of time (Hoot & Aronsky, 2008). In the context of an ED, while applications of queueing theory may allow for an increase in resources for staff and patients, such increases may not always improve efficiency nor adequately address the need to reduce overcrowding (Hoot & Aronsky, 2008; Hwang, Lipman & Kane, 2014; Lin, Patrick & Labeau, 2014). Demand for care in an ED constantly fluctuates. Outbreaks of a dangerous disease or large amounts of injured patients from a mass shooting may immediately deplete the capacity for an ED to make its resources available to everyone at the same time.

Nearly twenty years prior to the study conducted by Hoot and Aronsky (2008), Dickinson (1989) noted the inevitability of patient overcrowding in an ED due to the "unpredictable ebb and flow of emergency health care needs" (p. 270). However, despite its inevitability, patient overcrowding has a merely sporadic nature (Dickinson, 1989). Certainly, events such as influenza outbreaks and natural disasters create an influx of demand (Glaser et al., 2002). Yet, emergencies do not follow a schedule. Thus, ebbs and flows in patient numbers occur throughout different areas of an entire hospital. Even the best run ED can face periods of overcrowding, though this problem seems more like a rule rather than the exception. ED staff contributes as many of their own resources as possible depending on the specialized training received (Dickinson, 1989). Nurses spend their time providing ward care to admitted patients, while emergency physicians express frustration at the lack of available nurses to provide emergency care (Dickinson, 1989). Ambulance drivers receive reports from hospitals that an ED is full and that they must divert patients to a different and probably more distant hospital (Delgado et al., 2013; Schull et al., 2004).

Ironically, transporting ambulatory patients to a different hospital was an early solution to the problem of overcrowding (Dickinson, 1989). The major drawback to this solution was an increase in negative health outcomes for moderately to severely ill and injured patients denied access to care. Ambulance drivers do not have enough professional credential to maintain critically ill or injured patients in a moving vehicle. As a result, delays in receiving care caused by ambulance diversion to a different facility leads to further complications and even death (Delgado et al., 2013; Dickinson, 1989). Some hospitals understandably do not have enough resources or staffing to accommodate every patient with a severe illness or injury, though a scarcity in resources leads to hospitals either promoting an early discharge or borrowing beds from different units (Blom et al., 2014; Dickinson, 1989; Guttman et al., 2011; Hoot & Aronsky, 2008). While early discharges may help reduce ED overcrowding, they may lead to complications if patients have dormant symptoms of a potentially severe illness. Conversely, having enough beds to admit ED patients is critical for providing care to severely ill or injured patients.

A steady trend of patient overcrowding caused by the frequency of visits by non-urgent patients during certain times of the day in the absence of having access to primary care. While Dickinson (1989) argued that emergency medical care is essential and should remain open for public access, frequent flyer patients, inadequate staffing, inpatient boarding, and hospital bed shortages have all been implicated in overcrowding (Atzema et al., 2012; Bair, Song, Chen, & Morris, 2010; Brown et al., 2011; Hoot & Aronsky, 2008; Schull, Mandani & Fang, 2003). ED staff must prepare for any emergency through proper staffing. Patient overcrowding in an ED is a self-reinforcing cycle in which revenue lost to uninsured patients, diverted ambulances, and insured patients leaving without being seen (LWBS) creates staffing problems (Carron et al., 2014; Guttman et al., 2011; Hurwitz et al., 2014; Lovett et al., 2014; Sayah et al., 2014). Furthermore, inpatient boarding and hospital bed shortages confound the ability of ED staff to treat everyone requiring immediate medical attention.

Research that is more recent recognized the problem of providing timely care to patients without scheduled appointments to visit. The same research also noted how the problem of patient overcrowding is the result of an increase in ED closures that create challenges for meeting greater demands (Hurwitz et al., 2014). Operational efficiency dwindled as the result of ED closures leading to a rising problem in patient overcrowding. Using techniques from both queueing theory and operations research theory, Hurwitz and colleagues (2014) assessed a variety of patient flow outcomes by including factors like door-to-event times, propensity to leave without being seen (LWBS), ED occupancy level, dynamic staff, and use of resources.

The study found that patient overcrowding varies and requires solutions specific to individual hospitals. The availability of ED staff, however, presents the challenge of bottlenecks in patient flow management (Hurwitz et al., 2014). Reducing wait times in an ED may not, in other words, have an expected positive impact in terms of throughput measures.

Hospitals that redirect their resources to increase efficiency in providing care for patients with less severe illnesses, or injuries without delaying care for patients who have more acute illnesses or injuries (Hurwitz et al., 2014). Academic hospitals have lower bed availability that causes a bottleneck in patient flow (Crilly et al., 2014). Hence, hospitals that implement a scheduling system for non-urgent patients without a regular source of primary care have only limited improvements to providing efficient and effective care for patients with emergency medical needs (Hurwitz et al., 2014). Rather, shorter boarding times reduce ED overcrowding more effectively.

Scheduling systems for non-urgent patients who make frequent visits to an ED as a regular source of primary care may lead to improvement in patient satisfaction. However, some patients may argue that visiting an ED is a process of rational decision making given their unique circumstances related to the availability of health care facilities in their neighborhood. One study analyzed the use of appointment scheduling systems on patient satisfaction by using research through questionnaires on two different groups of patients (Zade et al., 2014). The first group analyzed included patients who used traditional systems of appointment scheduling and admission, leading the researchers to measure satisfaction prior to interventions by hospital staff. The second group analyzed included patients who used a model of appointment scheduling system to measure satisfaction after interventions by hospital staff. The study found that not only does introducing a scheduling increase patient satisfaction at some hospitals, scheduling systems help health professional improve decision-making processes (Zade et al., 2014).

Scheduling systems allow hospitals to meet the needs of more patients by having solutions in place for maintaining the quality of providing care to patients.

Prior to the use of a scheduling, the hospital studied had problems with ED overcrowding, declines in the quality of care facilities, a lack of staff on duty, and large gaps in time between arrival and discharge (Zade et al., 2014). Patient satisfaction was lowest especially regarding the behaviors of doctors and other ED staff towards patients. After the hospital implemented a scheduling system, patient satisfaction increased dramatically. The largest improvements in patient satisfaction were in the quality of care facilities, time between arrival and discharge, and number of ED staff on duty (Zade et al., 2014). Yet, despite improvements in patient satisfaction after implementing a scheduling system, limitations to the aforementioned study included patients arriving late for an appointment who also demanded immediate service. Other factors presenting limitations resulted from how some doctors were late for appointments with patients leading to lower levels of satisfaction in some instances. Results of this study suggested that health professional should make provisions for ensuring that they can meet with scheduled patients in a timely manner though they may need to treat patients with more acute illnesses or injuries (Zade et al., 2014). Health professionals may stretch their efforts too thinly when having to treat emergency patients while also having to treat scheduled patients who visit a hospital for routine care.

Admissions Policies and Effect on Patient Flow

A small amount of research highlighted the effects on admissions policies and effects on patient flow in an ED (Hung et al., 2014; Kang et al., 2014; Sayah et al., 2014). Admissions policies at some hospitals may actually delay the admission of patients into an intensive care unit (ICU), leading to adverse health outcomes (Hung et al., 2014). Delayed admission into an ICU has a strong correlation with a higher probability of mortality in patients as well as a correlation with use and expenditure of resources.

Optimal care depends on whether patients receive treatment in a timely manner, especially if they rely on ventilator (Hung et al., 2014). Patients who rely on ventilator support belong to different age groups and have different causes of the symptoms they experience. Delays in admission may result in patients having an out-of-hospital cardiac arrest (OHCA) or an unexpected in-hospital cardiac arrest (IHCA) if ED staff fail to perform routine checks every two hours because of patient overcrowding (Hung et al., 2014). Adverse health outcomes are even more likely if patients who rely on ventilator support wait more than four hours between arrival and admission because of patient overcrowding.

Because of the possibility that some patients may have adverse health outcomes after waiting more than six hours in an ED, hospitals may consider testing different sets of admissions policies for controlling patient flow and preventing bottlenecks between arrival and discharge times. One recent study tested four different types of admissions policies to use in an ED with the first type of policy determined by a group of attending physicians, residents, and physician extenders and subsequent types of admissions policies determined by attending physicians who admit patients, teams of providers, and attending physicians in an ED (Kang et al., 2014). The hospital studied had the first type of admissions policy as determined by a group of attending physicians, residents, and physician extenders, though all three alternatives types of admissions policies proved effective in reducing the length of stay (LOS) for patients (Kang et al., 2014). Under a new admissions policy, patients may spend between 1.4 and 2.5 hours less when waiting to receive admission into an ED. Patient flow improves dramatically with new admissions policies by decreasing the LOS of discharged patients by between five and 6.4 percent (Kang et al., 2014). The major implication of results for this study on reducing ED waiting times for patients in public hospitals of the Detroit metropolitan area is that an efficient admissions process can help reduce times between admissions. Another implication in terms of discharge is that ED staff should develop a working framework for implementing new admissions policies.

More notably, the number of patients who leave without being seen (LWBS) in public hospitals located of the Detroit metropolitan area are likely to decrease because of properly implementing new admissions policies. Sayah and colleagues (2014) conducted a pre- and post- intervention analysis to assess the impact of a process improvement project at a hospital in Cambridge, England by re-engineering the experiences of patients between arriving and departing from an ED. The main goals of the study were to improve patient flow by emphasizing patient-centered care; implement evidence-based best practices; integrate the use of improvement methodologies, tools, and measures; implement a multidisciplinary approach with a single solution; and explore causes of ED overcrowding.

Infrequent Events

EDs can experience overcrowding due to infrequent events that result in a large number of high-acuity emergencies in a very short time. While this is not the primary reason for patient overcrowding, it does challenge the abilities of a single ED. Influenza outbreaks are one of the most common reasons for sharp changes in demand for emergency care within a short period (Glaser et al., 2002). While primary care services may better assist patients with influenza and older patients, poor and uninsured patients have an increased risk for adverse health outcomes after treatment.

In a retrospective time series analysis conducted over the course of 40 months in the ED of various public hospitals in Toronto, Ontario, Canada, one study found a correlation between ambulance diversion and influenza outbreaks (Schull et al., 2003). The study indicated that 24.3 percent of ambulance drivers diverted from an overcrowded ED because of an influenza outbreak. A related study noted that during an influenza outbreak between 1997 and 1998 in the Los Angeles metropolitan area, ambulance diversions coincided with peak respiratory hospitalizations and deaths (Glaser et al., 2002). Patterns of patient over-crowding in an ED call into question the capability of current medical systems to handle regular influenza seasons (Glaser et al., 2002). The study by Russo (2006) confirmed the findings observed by Glaser and colleagues (2002) in addressing the importance of coordinating ambulatory services with hospitals, public health groups, and local governments to handle increases in ED use by patients without a regular source of primary care.

Coordinating ambulatory services with an ED during mass casualty events and natural disasters may help improve health outcomes for patients with acute illness or injury. Yet an ED that faces the problem of patient overcrowding on a frequent basis experiences compound effects because they lack the resources to coordinate services efficiently and effectively. One such strategy may be the utilization of multidisciplinary trauma centers at scenes of major disasters, as initially suggested by Dickinson (1989). However, one re-cent study argued that reducing ambulatory diversion may prove helpful for reducing patient overcrowd-ing despite the uncertainty of creating optimal solutions (Delgado et al., 2013). The study by Delgado and colleagues (2013) quantified throughput measures of tradeoff between ambulance diversion and waiting times for patients in an ED while it also evaluated the effect of reducing ambulance diversion on patient flow and evaluated an optimal diversion policy among multiple hospitals. Quantifying throughput mea-sures of ambulance diversion and waiting times for patients in an ED may involve diverting patients based on the number of boarded patients or in a waiting room rather than depending on the availability of beds (Delgado et al, 2013). However, the overall effect of ambulance diversion is small in that it decreases waiting times by only 30 minutes. Reductions in boarding time and length of stay (LOS) help to reduce ambulance diversion, thus decreasing ED waiting times further.

Patient flow interventions may include an ED fast track for patients with less acute illnesses or inju-ries along with a holding area to remove boarding patients from treatment spaces (Delgado et al., 2013). For patients who need lab work, one intervention for reducing ED waiting times includes decreased turnaround times from two hours to one hour. Canceling admissions for some patients without acute symptoms or injuries would lead to greater reductions in both ambulance diversion and ED waiting times by increasing the availability of beds (Delgado et al., 2013). The only major barrier preventing reductions in both ambulance diversions and ED waiting times is the lack of effective quality management strategies.

Hospitals without cooperative strategies for reducing ambulance diversions may ultimately resort to "pre-emptive" or "defensive" diversion and thus increase waiting times more significantly (Delgado et al., 2013). Cooperative strategies between ambulance drivers and ED staff may decrease ED waiting times that do not promote any increased value for patients.

Barriers to Accessing Primary Care

The added stress that mass casualty incidents and influenza outbreaks add to patient overcrowding provide clues for how to solve the problem of overcrowding, but the contemporary focus should rely on patient demographics lining up in overcrowded waiting rooms. Non-urgent, low-acuity patients are the focus of many studies in the research literature on patient overcrowding (Afilalo et al., 2004; Anderson & Karlberg, 2001; Brown et al., 2011; Dent et al., 2003; Durand et al., 2012; Gentile et al., 2010; Grumbach, Keane, & Bindman, 1993; Kellerman & Weinick, 2012; Liaw et al., 2014; Pitts et al., 2010; Rust et al., 2008; Schull et al., 2007).

Non-urgent ED use is part of a larger discussion on the links between medicine and politics, and that diverting non-urgent patients to general practitioners is part of a political strategy (Afilalo et al., 2004). Thus, researchers may incur substantial benefits from understanding the reasons why some populations have barriers to accessing primary care.

Diverting patients to a general practitioner may have benefits for patients with emerging health problems. In 2010, only 42 percent of the 354 million annual visits to a hospital for acute care were for a regular physician whereas nearly28 percent of regular hospital visits were to an ED. Meanwhile, 20 percent of visits were to a specialist and seven percent of visits were to an outpatient department (Pitts et al., 2010). Fewer than five percent of doctors have the professional title of emergency physician, though they handle nearly 25 percent of all patients receiving treatment for urgent or emergency care. More than half of the patients that visit an ED to receive treatment for urgent or emergency care did not have insurance in 2010, though recent provisions for improving the American health care system have an overarching goal of promoting greater access to acute care (Pitts et al., 2010). Patient-centered medical care and accountable care organizations are only two of the many possible interventions worth considering. These interventions promote greater access to primary care on a regular basis and improve health outcomes where applicable.

A common reason attributed for the use of an ED during non-urgent medical events is a lack of access to primary care services, a problem that dates to earlier studies on patient overcrowding in an ED (Dickinson, 1989). In another early study of 700 patients in an urban public ED, Grumbach and colleagues (1993) measured and compared the variables of access to alternative sources of medical care, clinical appropriateness of ED use, and the willingness of patients to use non-emergency services. Nearly half of the patients (45 percent) cited a lack of access to primary care as the reason for using an ED, while only 13 percent of patients who visited an ED had conditions considered clinically appropriate (Grumbach et al., 1993). The results of this study suggested that patients with regular access to primary care used an ED more appropriately than patients without a similar degree of access did. However, 38 percent of patients suggested a willingness to trade their wait position in an ED for an appointment with a physician within three days of admission (Grumbach et al., 1993). The suggestions made by this relatively early study on the correlation between the lack of access to primary care and the frequent use of an ED implied that referrals may help patients with less acute illnesses or injuries. However, referrals only help to the extent that patients with a lower socioeconomic status gain more frequent access to primary care.

Ten years later, a retrospective review by Dent and colleagues (2003) tested the hypothesis that "frequent flyer" patients without regular access to primary care are more likely to visit an ED for general practice. The research setting was an academic hospital in the inner city of Melbourne, Australia. Results indicated an average of 26 visit per patient between December 1996 and April 2002 (Dent et al., 2003). Out of those visits per patient to an ED, only 59.5 percent were deemed medically appropriate for receiving emergency care (Dent et al., 2003).

Time of day was an important variable when accounting for business hours of most primary care facilities. Concurrently, 28.5 percent of patients were the heaviest ED users who presented symptoms of illnesses and injuries more suitable for a general practitioner to treat.

Because of its location, 40.9 percent of patients who visited the ED studied in inner city Melbourne were homeless while 26.5 percent of these patients had psychiatric issues or were under the extreme influence of alcohol and drugs (Dent et al., 2003). Unfortunately, 90 patients who were the most "frequent flyers" of an ED died during the study period. Results of this study suggested that most patients admitted into a hospital located in an urban, inner city setting do not technically qualify as needing to receive emergency treatment. However, diverting "frequent flyer" patients to general practice may not always lead to improved health outcomes for patients because of the severity and complexity of the cases presented to an ED on a reoccurring basis (Dent et al., 2003). Because the ED studied was inside of an academic hospital, reductions of patient overcrowding might not prove conducive to having positive effects on the outcomes of "frequent flyer" patients because academic hospitals often do not have adequate resources for admission and treatment on a regular basis.

Outside of the inner city context, one study of five different EDs in the Canadian province of Québec found that primary reasons why some patients were visited an ED more frequently included perception of need, referrals and follow-up visits, and familiarity with and trust in ED staff (Afilalo et al., 2004).

Diversion strategies for referring patients to a general practitioner often fail, implying that a multi-faceted approach is more appropriate for improving patient flow. Strategies for intervening in the type of care that patients receive if they have persistent barriers to accessing primary care may alleviate some of the negatives effects on a health care system (Afilalo et al., 2004). Yet the true impact on a health care system is worth evaluating for continued research in the future. If "frequent flyer" patients without regular access to primary care do not pose cost burdens, they may not always pose a contributing factor to the problem of overcrowding (Afilalo et al., 2004). Future research would need to evaluate the impact of frequent flyer patients on a health care system as a whole. If patients who visit an ED do not have adverse health outcomes after staff diverts care to a general practitioner via ambulance, then the problems of this strategy present a non-issue.

Patients who do not have regular access to primary care and who frequently visit and ED to receive care are what one study cited as "low-complexity patients" who contribute to delays and overcrowding (Schull, Kiss, & Szalal, 2007). Low-complexity patients typically arrive by ambulance, have a low acuity in symptoms of illness or injury, and are often discharged within eight hours of arriving (Schull et al., 2007). However, a later study presented conflicting results in noting a reduction in the number of low-complexity patients who visit an ED does not significantly decrease waiting times for other patients nor does a similar reduction lessen the effects of overcrowding (Rust et al., 2008). The same study found that low-complexity patients who arrive at an ED have increased the wait times for other patients by only 8.6 minutes. In any case, not all patients fit the definition of low-complexity patient because of the probability for diversion to a general practitioner at different care facility (Schull et al., 2007). Diverting low- complexity patients does not decrease the safety risks nor does it lead to adverse health outcomes. Rather, diverting low-complexity patients to another unit or to another facility does not lead to significant changes.

One important benefit of having a regular source of primary care is cost-effectiveness for patients, ED staff, and an entire health care system (Rust et al., 2008). Some of the barriers to accessing primary care as identified by patients include household income and educational level. Patients with lower incomes are more likely to visit an ED than patients with higher incomes while patients with less than a high school diploma or with less than a secondary education were also more likely to visit an ED (Rust et al., 2008). Health status also affects the frequency of ED use by patients without regular access to primary care. Patients who already have poor health conditions were reportedly twice as likely to visit an ED if they did not already have regular access to primary care (Rust et al., 2008).

However, barriers to timely access, such as having to visit an ED outside of regular clinic hours, lead some patients to make frequent visits to an ED. Interventions for improving access to primary care for patients who frequently visit and ED involve the use of strategies such as open access scheduling, that have the potential to increase patient satisfaction, improve perceptions of patients having regular access to primary care, and improve efficiency to provide continuous care. Yet even when such interventions lead to improvements for patients without regular access to primary care, patients may continue to visit an ED with the same frequency (Rust et al., 2008). Providing greater access to primary care is not the same as providing timely and effective access to care. The implications for health policy are that a health care system can work towards making noticeable improvements in the health outcomes of patients with more acute illnesses or injuries.

Patient-centered care is one intervention worth considering reducing ED overcrowding in the future as partially caused by patients with barriers to access primary care on a regular basis (Pitts et al., 2010; Rust et al., 2008). Patient-centered care may emphasize the delivery of after- hours care and the setting of clear expectations to ensure that patients receive quality care (Pitts et al., 2010). Here, general practitioners are more likely qualified to supervise after-hours care and an ED can pay closer attention to more acute cases as they arrive.

Fragmented relationships in health care between external providers and hospitals pose significant barriers for patients to access primary care on a regular basis, as noted by an earlier study (Anderson & Karlberg, 2001). However, more studies that are recent highlighted demographic factors related to race and ethnicity as a barrier for accessing primary care on a regular basis and visiting an ED for minor illnesses or injuries more frequently (Brown et al., 2011). African-Americans are more likely to access health care by visiting an ED than Caucasians, yet the patterns are unclear as to why this is the case. Some African-Americans reported a preference for visiting the ED as a source for having access to primary care, though no significant barriers to access, including insurance, were noted (Brown et al., 2011). Within a six- month period, African-Americans reported less compounding symptoms and reported a lesser need for hospitalization, though this group of patients was at least twice as likely to visit an ED.

Perceptions of patient "misuse."

Increases in demands for access to primary care by visiting an ED constitutes as "misuse" by patients seeking care for minor illnesses or injuries (Durand et al., 2012). In one study that involved conducting semi-structured interviews with patients, three important themes emerged from the data as reasons why some patients actually prefer visiting an ED—an ED fulfills health care needs, patients have barriers to accessing primary care on a regular basis, and convenience (Durand et al., 2012). Some patients prefer to visit an ED for their primary care needs because they felt overwhelmed by having to schedule appointments with a number of referred specialists whereas other patients had difficulties in scheduling an appointment as soon as deemed necessary (Durand et al., 2012). The findings suggest that hospitals can provide patients with greater access to technical facilities within an ED to improve the efficiency of having to schedule appointments with specialists after receiving an initial consultation.

The fulfillment of health care needs leads patients to feel a reduction in anxiety about the prognosis of their health condition, even if they knew that their symptoms were not life- threatening (Durand et al., 2012). Barriers to accessing primary care providers on a regular basis led patients to feel anxious when they encountered difficulties in setting a timely appointment, thus leading them to seek care in an ED. Lack of time during regular business hours also posed substantial barriers to setting a timely appointment with a regular primary care provider either before or after a workday (Dent et al., 2003; Durand et al., 2012). Patients who had a lack of time during regular business hours perceived that seeking care in an ED was a savvy consumer move by claiming adequate knowledge about the health care system and the services available to them in their area (Durand et al., 2012). Because of this perception, patients expressed the opinion that they were able to access an ED as an alternative to receiving treatment from a primary care physician while patients also opined that they could translate perceptions about the health care system into practical choices.

Patients in the study by Durand and colleagues (2012) identified specific advantages to visiting an ED as alternative to visiting a primary care provider on a regular basis. One advantage was the availability of resources, especially greater access to laboratory and radiography tests that are not often available in a primary care facility (Durand et al., 2012).

Patients who more frequently visited an ED than they visited a primary care provider indicated perceptions of relative convenience. For some patients, an ED is similar to a "one-stop" shopping center where a wider variety of technical facilities and medications are available (Durand et al., 2012, p. 529). The perceived advantage of convenience eases patient anxiety about having to make multiple appointments to different facilities after receiving a referral to a specialist from a primary care physician. Patients with less severe illnesses or injuries that may require the use of an X-ray, a CT scan, or surgical intervention perceived receiving more efficient care than they would have received from a primary care physician and from referrals to specialists.

On the other hand, semi-structured interviews with health professionals led to four themes emerging from the data. Health professionals noted problems in defining a non-urgent visit, explaining to patients why they should not use an ED on a frequent basis for non-urgent complaints, consequences of non-urgent visits to an ED, and solutions to counter the tendency for patients without regular primary care to visit an ED on a frequent basis (Durand et al., 2012). Health professionals recognize the lack of clarity in defining what constitutes a non-urgent visit by patients to an ED, though they often define non-urgent cases as "minor medical problem[s]" that are "non-acute [and] non-life-threatening" (Durand et al., 2012, p. 525). Health professionals made a distinction between the concepts of "non-urgency" as opposed to "vital urgency," in which the former does not require immediate attention and implies that a delay of several hours will not lead to adverse health outcomes in patients (Durand et al., 2012, p. 525-7). Health professionals with professional experience working in an ED made a further distinction between cases considered "non-urgent" as opposed to those considered "inappropriate" by emphasizing the severity of a medical problem in reference to vital signs (Durand et al., 2012, p. 527). Cases considered "inappropriate" by health professionals with ED experience defined the term according to the social and psychological conditions of patients, as well as time of visit and availability of health care in an ED (Durand et al., 2012). As with previous studies, health professionals believe that lack of access to primary care influences patients to visit an ED more frequently than patients who have access that is more "appropriate".

Health professionals believe that patients who visit an ED for non-urgent complaints do not know how to make proper health care decisions by claiming full agency in the decision- making process for receiving treatment (Durand et al., 2012). Health care professionals believe that patients who make frequent visits to an ED as an alternative to primary care "abuse the system" (Durand et al., 2012, p. 531). Medicine is an apparent casualty in perceived abuse of the health care system by patients, as health professionals perceive that non-urgent patients want services and medication immediately are not responsible for their health. However, health professionals note the cost for hospitals to provide care for non-urgent patients who make frequent visits (Durand et al., 2012). Accordingly, patients are not aware of the costs associated with using services provided by an ED because of not having to pay for services during consultation. Patients receive treatment first before receiving a bill later if health insurance applies but not all health insurance cover all fees.

Health professionals with ED experience noted further that non-urgent patients decreased access to patients with actual emergencies (Durand et al., 2012). Non-urgent patients reduce the quality of care for patients with actual emergencies by creating delays in waiting times, diagnoses and treatments, and care while non-urgent patients also create a "spillover effect" that leads to an increased level of frustration among ED staff (Durand et al., 2012, p. 531). As a result, health professionals may have the impression that they cannot perform the services for which they were originally trained to do.

Solutions for reducing the number of ED visits for non-urgent patients would need to provide educational opportunities regarding the appropriate use of a health care system so that they can make decisions that are more rational from the perspective of health professionals (Durand et al., 2012). Solutions may also include a restructuring of the health care system by keeping primary care facilities open later while other solutions may consider hiring an ED "gatekeeper" who must have authorization from primary care providers to admit non-urgent patients into an ED (Durand et al., 2012, p. 531). Further, some health professionals suggest that a few patients incur financial penalties for their "inappropriate" use of the health care system by "misusing" the services provided by ED staff.

The study by Durand and colleagues (2012) highlighted the seemingly fragmented nature of the health care system as a whole in terms of relationships between health professionals and patients. Specifically, gaps in perceptions led researchers to emphasize patient behaviors as health professionals emphasized the acuity and urgency of medical problems. Patients especially emphasized what they perceived as rational reasons for visiting an ED as a source of primary care (Durand et al., 2012). Patients argued that a lack of access to immediate health care resources and the context in which their medical problems occur warrant frequent visits to an ED. Based on the findings, implications for future research should investigate ways to improve ED overcrowding and decrease frequent "misuse" by patients who lack regular access to primary care. Future research would analyze how the demand for access to health care provides a correlative link to health professionals use decision-making processes in handling patients who arrive at a hospital without a scheduled appointment.

Countering professional claims of patient misuse.

Patients who most frequently use an ED do so largely because of an inability to access primary care services, but such a condition encompasses many situations. Poverty, lack of insurance, lack of access to adequate insurance, and lack of access to timely primary care services incentivize and necessitate the use of an ED. Waiting lines are generally longer in poor, urban areas. 21.6 percent of patients enrolled in Medicaid used an ED as a regular source of care (Liaw et al., 2014). Among those without insurance who also did not have regular access to primary care, 24.1 percent used an ED for more than half of their ambulatory visits, though 7.8 percent of patients who had private insurance and who did not have regular access to primary care used an ED for ambulatory visits (Liaw et al., 2014). The results of this study led to the conclusion that mostly the uninsured and patients enrolled in Medicaid were most likely to visit an ED as a source of primary care.

In a demographic look at Medicaid recipients, Lowe and colleagues (2009) found that patients enrolled in Medicaid were 12 percent less likely to use an ED on a regular basis to access primary care. Brown and colleagues (2011) found that in one tertiary care ED, African Americans were two times as likely as Caucasians to use an ED as a regular sources of access to primary care. Afilalo and colleagues (2004) found that throughout five tertiary care EDs in Québec, non-urgent patients were younger, had better health, were less likely to arrive by ambulance, and were less often admitted to a hospital ward.

Such a wide variety of demographic groups who use an ED indicates one common theme of lacking regular access to adequate or timely primary care. Rust and colleagues (2008) found five common access barriers including not connecting with hospital staff after, for instance, waiting on hold for too long; not receiving an appointment when needed; waiting too long to see a doctor, limited hours of some services, and lack of transportation. The noted factors coincide with other studies that surveyed reasons that non-urgent patients with low-acuity medical issues presented to the ED. Afilalo and colleagues (2004) found that accessibility, perception of need, and referrals from primary care providers were of relatively similar importance for non-urgent patients. Howard and colleagues (2005) showed similar data, with inability to secure an appointment with a primary care provider, referrals from primary care provider, and perceptions that receiving services at an ED would take less time than waiting to see a doctor at a primary care facility were the primary reasons given by non-urgent ED patients. As access to primary care services appears to decline, access to care via an EDs increased, though not for all patients.

Measures to address non-urgent utilization of the ED for access the primary care services have been explored. An earlier study found that 38 percent of ED patients surveyed would likely trade a long ED wait line for a direct referral to a primary care facility (Grumbach et al., 1993).

Similarly, a more recent study found that using an ED medical screening exam to identify non- urgent patients seeking regular access to primary care resulted in an 85 percent satisfaction rate for those deemed eligible for direct referral (Stone et al., 2013). Of those referrals, only 17 percent made a return visit to an ED within three months.

Some hospitals may extend direct referral programs to external primary care facilities. In their examination of a primary care referral program in France, Gentile and colleagues (2010) found that 68 percent of ED patients were willing see a doctor in a primary care facility. The study noted that referring patients to primary care facilities located near a hospital or near where patients live, is an appropriate response to the growing demand for access to health care (Gentile et al., 2010). Similarly, referrals to patient-centered care in primary care facilities among patients with chronic illnesses led to a decreased likelihood of having delayed care, thus leading to fewer ED visits (Hearld & Alexander, 2012). Therefore, increasing access to primary care services by having a referral system in place is an effective way to decrease ED overcrowding.

However, some studies indicated that patients seeking primary care do not affect the length of wait times in an ED. Low-complexity patients only have a negligible effect on the increase in ED wait times (Schull et al., 2007). Every set of ten low-complexity patients arriving every eight hours led to an average increased wait time of 5.4 minutes and an increased wait time averaging 2.1 minutes for medium- and high-complexity patients to see a physician.

Comparatively, most patients who used an ED most frequently by the heaviest use were not suitable for treatment by a general practitioner (Dent et al., 2003). Diversion to primary care facilities would promote adverse health outcomes in patients.

While studies as those just mentioned are dated and few, they reflect the complexity of debates in how to improve a health care system as much as they also pay attention to the problem of patient overcrowding in an ED. Studies that are more recent confirm the findings of earlier studies in many ways, though the former have more nuanced implications for physicians and health policy in the context of recent changes to insurance schemes that promote greater access to primary care. The following section draws attention to how recent studies recognized a correlation between ED overcrowding and adverse health outcomes that reduce the overall quality of care.

Health Outcomes of Patients

A substantial portion of the literature indicated a direct correlation between ED overcrowding events and adverse health outcomes and reductions in the quality of care (Atzema et al., 2012; Bernstein et al., 2009; Blom et al., 2014; Guttman et al., 2011; Henriksen, Brabrand, & Lassen, 2014; Hung et al., 2014; Singer et al., 2011). Six domains of quality of care—safety, patient-centeredness, timeliness, efficiency, effectiveness, and equity—as reported by the Institute of Medicine (IOM) were useful in juxtaposing against a series of case studies, cohort studies, and clinical trials to address the effects of ED overcrowding on clinically oriented outcomes (COO; Bernstein et al., 2009). Patient overcrowding in an ED leads to increased mortality rates. Patient overcrowding also leads to longer treatment times for patients with pneumonia or acute pain. While it also leads to a higher probability of patients leaving the ED without anyone seeing them against medical advice (Bernstein et al., 2009; Carron et al., 2014; Lovett et al., 2014). One study suggested that ED overcrowding has a correlation with objective clinical goals and clinically important processes of providing care (Bernstein et al., 2009). The ability for ED staff to treat patients with time-sensitive conditions safely and effectively involves having to making compromises to health outcomes because of overcrowding.

Patients who wait in an ED without attendance by staff receive what some researchers identified as "incomplete emergency care" (Carron et al., 2014). Some patients may have already completed paperwork required for admissions and received an initial evaluation by a triage nurse, though other patients leave against medical advice (LAMA) during their stay in an ED (Carron et al., 2014). At the same time, some patients leave without receiving an assignment to a triage nurse (Lovett et al., 2014). Patients LAMA either during a diagnostic period when waiting for an X-ray exam, or they may leave by refusing treatment or hospitalization. Patients who "leave without being seen" (LWBS) and who "leave against medical advice" (LAMA) are often considered "missed opportunities" by ED staff and an entire health care system (Carron et al., 2014). Regardless of their status, LWBS and LAMA patients have an indirect correlation with patient overcrowding. Not all LWBS and LAMA patients leave because of overcrowding.

ED staff must adhere to internal policies when they have LAMA patients, as these patients must have a proper medical contact and signatures on admissions paperwork by patients, nurse, and physicians in charge (Carron et al., 2014). Paperwork for LAMA patients typically involves recording the time of departure, any clear clinical elements, and the reason cited for leaving, along with any possible recommendations given for follow-up treatment. For LWBS patients, on the other hand, ED staff does not have an opportunity to document why they left, though nursing and medical records may fill in some missing information. LWBS patients often have a greater severity of illness or injury (Lovett et al., 2014). To account for demographics, most LWBS patients are young men with a lesser severity of illness or injury.

LWBS patients visited an ED more frequently as a source of receiving primary care while they are the most likely to leave without receiving an assignment to a triage nurse (Lovett et al., 2014). Because of the noted factors, LWBS patients face more adverse health outcomes.

Similarly, some of the research found a correlation between ED boarding and negative health outcomes for patients (Singer et al., 2011). Prolonged ED boarding entails an increased length of stay (LOS). Both factors lead to a significant decrease in the quality of care patients receive (Bukhari et al., 2014). Factors that influence this correlation include patient arrival time, length of time before an assessment by a triage nurse and later by a doctor, arrival time to a specific area in a hospital, length of time in consultation, length of time to conduct a laboratory or radiological investigation, and patient discharge time (Bukhari et al., 2014). Negative health outcomes including mortality had a strong correlation with increases in boarding times while LOS had a similar correlation (Singer et al., 2011).

Causes of patient overcrowding were found in greater demands for care and resources, insufficient or inadequate staffing, and a lack of bed space. Patient overcrowding leads to delays in patients in receiving important medications, resulting in complications from lack of proper treatment after evaluation by a triage nurse and doctors (Singer et al., 2011). Competing demands for care and resources leads to an overload in an ED department and has negative consequences for the entire health care system. At the same time, patients with more severe illnesses or injuries may have to wait longer to receive care because patients with less severe illnesses or injuries take less time to evaluate, treat, and discharge (Singer et al., 2011). The correlation between patient overcrowding and adverse health outcomes are more complex when accounting for factors like patient satisfaction; however, solutions are necessary for reducing or eliminating ED boarding altogether.

Solutions for reducing ED boarding time to decrease LOS may include a close monitoring of the triage system and increasing the availability, access, and time for patients to receive specialty consultations (Newton et al., 2014). The variables of wait time in an ED and LOS have practical use for researchers to measure and ensure patient safety, though longer wait times have a strong correlation with a higher triage level that denotes lesser severity of symptoms or injuries, ED occupancy, and "walk-in" patients (Newton et al., 2014). Other correlative factors for increased ED waiting times include ethnicity and gender that raise issues of access to timely care in conjunction with racial and gender discrimination, language barriers, and cultural competence among ED staff (Newton et al., 2014). In some cases where patients arrive at an ED with psychiatric symptoms in need of treatment, limited staff availability and the time of day when patients arrive—e.g., late evening versus early morning—to receive assessments have a correlation with longer LOS (Newton et al., 2014). Patients with psychiatric needs typically wait longer to receive care than other patients in an ED. The median waiting in an ED was ten minutes longer compared with other patients at times when an ED did not have overcrowding. However, patients with mental illness did not wait as long in an ED during periods of overcrowding (Atzema et al., 2012). All of the noted factors suggest that ED staff should devise strategies for ensuring timely treatment and quality of care.

Longer LOS has a correlation with the number of consultations and the number of laboratory investigations psychiatric patients during a visit to an ED (Newton et al., 2014). Longer LOS also has a correlation with a lack of access to specialized services, but does not necessarily a need for quality improvement (Newton et al., 2014). Rather, the length of time to accessing resources in an ED is a more critical variable, suggesting that every ED needs to ensure timely access to assessments and treatments. Patients arriving at an ED when it was already overcrowded events were five percent greater likelihood of mortality, had a longer LOS, and experienced a one percent increase in healthcare-related costs per admission (Sun et al., 2013). A cohort analysis of non-federal, acute care hospitals in California indicated a strong correlation between ED overcrowding and an increase in overhead costs totaling $17 million admitted into an ED within this hospital system (Sun et al., 2013). While the causes and effects of ED overcrowding remain varied it is evident that ED overcrowding is a good indicator of poor health outcomes.

Despite the recent research literature on the health outcomes of patients visiting an ED, a gap in the research is present in discussions of whether in-hospital occupancy has a correlation with early discharge from an ED. A two-year retrospective analysis of all data on ED visits to a general hospital in southern Sweden found a significant association between in-hospital occupancy and a decreased odds ratio for admission (Blom et al., 2014). An implication of the results from this study was that patients who may benefit from in-patient care actually received inadequate care in outpatient settings during times of ED overcrowding (Blom et al., 2014).

Another implication from the results was that some physicians admit patients who would likely have better health outcomes in an outpatient setting, even during times when ED overcrowding is high and when more beds are likely available (Blom et al., 2014). In this context, physicians expose patients to hazards and health risks as they use resources that are better left for others.

Quality Improvement (QI)

The breadth of literature regarding ED overcrowding has pushed many hospitals to develop QI measures in an attempt to decrease patient overcrowding through internal and external quality assurance measures. The medical community, however, has been slow to implement such measures. Earlier studies noted three general approaches to developing quality assurance programs that emphasized structural issues, evaluations of health outcomes, and documentation of processes in delivering care. Quality assurance programs are necessary parts of health care delivery in hospitals around the world, and are popular among administrators who see quality assurance as a means of providing efficient and effective care and resources to patients. Yet the health outcomes of patients are difficult to assess in cases where outcomes do not have a strong correlation with the type of care provided. Some patients have positive health outcomes regardless of the care they receive.

The processes of how patients receive care are more subjective than they are precise measurements (Oberklaid et al., 1991). Some interventions designed to improve the quality of care that patients receive do not always fit with intended goals of promoting positive health outcomes. While decreases in ED wait times, admission rates, and number of laboratory investigations may lead to more positive health outcomes in patients, some of the processes used to make the goals of quality improvement more likely have counterproductive aspects.

Thorough evaluations of each patient who visits an ED are important for ensuring positive health outcomes. Health care providers hold a high degree of accountability for ensuring that patients receive care based on current, appropriate, and optimal procedures. However, as noted by many earlier and recent studies, maintaining standards of care in an ED poses significant challenges for maintaining quality and ensuring positive health outcomes (Oberklaid et al., 1991). Doctors and nurses work under constant pressure to see patients as quickly as possible and ensure that their conditions remain stable or indicate improvement. Doctors and nurses also have uneven workloads, leading many EDs to have a disproportionate amount of junior staff with relatively little experience. The rotation of doctors and nurses in an ED happens only for limited periods, and patients do not receive opportunities to learn from health professionals about how they may better access primary care facilities (Oberklaid et al., 1991). Hence, questions of how patients receive quality care in an ED continue to remain despite earlier studies presenting a case for needed improvements to decrease overcrowding.

Quality assurance programs are relatively new developments in the healthcare industry as the result of legislation on health maintenance organizations (HMOs) in the 1970s (Graff et al., 2002). Prior to this legislation, the health care industry seemed hesitant to adopt policies mandating improvements in a system for delivering care to patients. Yet as legislation passed, quality assurance programs developed as part of external regulatory requirements in health care (Graff et al., 2002). Along with the health care industry, nearly every other industry underwent similar changes to ensure a customer-driven "quality revolution" (Graff et al., 2002, p. 1091).

Manufacturing and services sectors developed measures of quality assurance and adapted them to critical work processes as central business strategies necessary for maintaining a competitive advantage at the organizational level. Market fluctuations and high-profile national reports lead nearly every industry to continuously develop measures for improving the quality of products and services provided to customers (Graff et al., 2002). In turn, the health care industry is part of the movement to develop continued measures for improving the quality of care and services delivered to patients.

While quality assurance in the health care industry was formerly a more external mechanism for developing critical business strategies, most clinical organizations find that they need to make continued improvements (Graff et al., 2002). Quality assurance is now more of an internal process of ensuring that business strategies remain in compliance with the requirements needed for: developing skills and training among hospital staff, using new information technologies, adapting to changes in workflows and routines, and changing a management focus that ultimately leads to a change in organizational culture (Graff et al., 2002). Quality assurance programs that lead to a change in organizational culture must maintain a commitment to recognizing that change is a necessary component of ensuring organizational survival. However, measuring improvements in the quality of health care system has inextricable links to measuring improvements in the health outcomes of patients who visit primary care facilities versus an ED on a regular basis.

Measuring Quality in the Health Care Industry

Quality assurance programs in most other industries emphasize the customer experience that judges the ability for providers of different services to meet or exceed expectations (Graff et al., 2002). Measuring quality of service in the healthcare industry can include the use of data elements describing an individual aspect of medical care that most customers would consider essential for delivering interventions that result in positive health outcomes. Customers that visit an ED include patients, family members, admitting and consulting physicians, hospital administration, payers, and purchasers. Sometimes, the needs and priorities for each types of customer are in alignment, though most needs are not (Graff et al., 2002). Reducing ED waiting times and LOS is a major concern among patients, family members, and hospital administration in the health care industry, though these issues are less important for payers. Reducing the use of expensive diagnostic tests and medications hold more importance for payers and purchasers but have less importance for patients (Graff et al., 2002). However, all parties in the health care

industry benefit when patients receive the highest quality of care based on evidence-based practices.

The primary mission of emergency medicine is the assurance of positive health outcomes and the highest possible survival rates. At the same time, providing comfort and reassurance to patients by providing ongoing information regarding the status of their condition is another important factor to ensure quality of care in the health care industry (Francis, Spies, & Kerner, 2008). Yet, because the ED is a very complex environment, the current state of patient overcrowding has a cause in an overemphasis on internal organizational processes.

Nevertheless, a broad customer base for receiving emergency medical services results from a complex network of supply and demand. Best practices for ensuring positive health outcomes in patients may appear counterproductive to other customers of health services. The burden of proof in ensuring quality outcomes in the health care industry is on hospital staff.

Earlier studies used three dimensions for measuring quality assurance in the health care industry. The first dimension of *clinical quality* helps the health care industry analyze the degree to which the types of care delivered runs congruent with evidence-based practices and that health outcomes can easily compare with benchmarking data (Graff et al., 2002). Measuring clinical quality accounts for safety, effectiveness, timeliness, and equity. In terms of overall effectiveness, these factors of accountability suggest that hospitals and ED staff strive towards reducing the underuse of effective care for patients with illnesses that are more acute or injuries while hospitals and ED staff also strive towards reducing the overuse of care better left to primary care providers (Graff et al., 2002). The factor of equity ensures that all patients have equal access to health care.

The second dimension of *service quality* entails measuring the degree to which care meets the expectations of patients by accounting for the factor of patient-centered care (Graff et al., 2002). One way that hospitals and ED staff can emphasize making improvements to service quality is in administering a survey before and after interventions to reduce ED waiting times.

The final dimension of *cost efficiency* involves measuring the amount of medical benefits and dividing them by the cost of each services provided (Graff et al., 2002). Hospitals and ED staff may consider comparing how efficiently they treat patients with less severe illnesses or injuries against how efficiently they treat patients with more severe conditions.

Despite the dimensions for measuring quality assurance in the health care industry, barriers include a lack of commitment from senior management for improving the organizational culture (Graff et al., 2002). Access to data presents another significant barrier for measuring quality assurance and marking improvements because most hospital and ED staff function used transaction-based information technologies designed for billing and for accessing laboratory and radiology data on individual patients (Graff et al., 2002). Linking multiple data systems across different departments in a hospital remains a difficult task.

Aggregating patient data and receiving accurate information in electronic formats is difficult in most environments. For the health care industry, integrating the functions of clinical, quality, administrative, and information technology (IT) has clear limitations for quality assurance (Graff et al., 2002; Hudson et al., 2014). Quality assurance programs usually entail the hiring of a staff member who managed large quantities of disparate data, though a staff member who manages quality in the health care industry maintains a transaction-based system that emphasizes improvements made to cost efficiency.

Few health institutions recognize quality assurance as a critical business strategy in recognizing how IT functions view managers of quality assurance as essential customers of the health care industry (Graff et al., 2002; Hudson et al., 2014). Quality assurance requires accuracy of measurements and adjustments for differences in health care environments and

patient populations. Each ED has its own unique set of circumstances depending on the conditions that patients have when they arrive. ED staff must determine the severity of an illness or injury before determining whether admission of patients is necessary (Graff et al., 2002).

However, most patients who receive treatment in an ED have substantially improved health outcomes.

Use of IT Services to Reduce Patient Overcrowding

The use of information and communication technologies (ICTs) is more critical for delivering health care services to patients without insurance (Bhatnagar, 2014; Morgareidge, Cai, & Jia, 2014; Rado et al., 2014). Improvements in quality assurance will continue to involve making the process of providing care more efficient while similar improvements will also continue to emphasize factors such as accountability and transparency. Some hospitals do not have the appropriate ICTs to improve efficiency in delivering care to patients (Bhatnagar, 2014). Applications of digital tools may allow hospital administration to aid in creating optimal designs for improving efficiency in ED facilities to reduce capital and operational costs and improve organizational performance (Morgareidge et al., 2014; Rado et al., 2014). Yet ensuring that different populations receive equity in treatment may necessarily depend on the authority of local public health officials.

While some rural populations may need to depend on county, regional, or state public health officials, urban populations face similar problems depending on neighborhood or proximity to public health officials (Bhatnagar, 2014). Information systems (IS) management remains critical for public health officials to maintain patient records of services received in the health care industry. IS management also retains several other functional purposes such as: monitoring the delivery of service, evaluating satisfaction levels in patients after receiving services, identifying gaps in the delivery of health care services, and responding appropriately to concerns of inadequate supply, lack of community involvement, and the need to promote further training (Bhatnagar, 2014). For ED and hospital staff, managing the health records of patients may seem easier said or written than done, though some health care systems outside of the United States have successfully integrated ICTs for community health workers to help patients receive more regular access to primary care.

In rural Ethiopia, community health workers use ICTs for mobile phones to register patients, create appointment reminders, and manage supply inventory (Bhatnagar, 2014; Otto, 2012). While the use of ICTs in Ethiopia via mobile phones has some benefits, actual implementation is a long-term process that may take many years to achieve full quality assurance in delivering positive health outcomes to patients who visit an ED and who have more severe illnesses or injuries (Bhatnagar, 2012). Improvements in the delivery of health care services through the use of community-oriented mobile phone technologies, such as that in rural populations of Ethiopia.

Accordingly, some of the research literature identified health care-based QI measures by controlling for structure, process, and outcomes. The standards of clinical quality, service quality, and cost efficiency have their basis in goals for benchmarking a maximum wait time.

Applicable standards have a noticeable impact in terms of a decrease in (LWBS) patients, increasing time-to-admission, and decreasing ambulance diversion (Burstin et al., 1999; Francis et al., 2008; Graff et al., 2002). Strengthening QI strategies ED outcomes should rely on both internal and external stressors that hinder the efficient delivery of care to patients.

QI Strategies

As hospitals consider implementing QI strategies to improve care, service, and cost, the greatest emphasis in their use is on benchmarking and data tracking in relation to patient overcrowding (Weiss et al., 2006). An early study observed wider compliance with guidelines for providing care to patients after implementing small interventions EDs of public hospitals in Massachusetts (Burstin et al., 1999). Compliance to guidelines led to a significant improvement in ED staff compliance and increased patient reported measures. An emphasis on benchmarking led to the consideration of many different strategies aimed at identifying and predicting patient overcrowding based on varying degrees of success at satisfying benchmark goals.

Ding and colleagues (2010) combined patient, clinical, temporal, and crowding factors into a quintile regression and determined that such an approach was useful for estimating the service completion experience of ED patients during normal and overcrowded periods.

McCarthy and colleagues (2011) took this a step further and found that measuring ED overcrowding at a daily level actually masked the variation in crowding that occurs in a full 24- hour period. The best metric, they concluded, is a discrete time survival analysis through which a correlation between monthly and annual data to time-specific situations may be identified (McCarthy et al., 2011). Thus, relying on patients simultaneously presenting to an ED could not provide reliable indicator of unsafe waiting times (Berg et al., 2014). Instead, the research examines other factors such as ambulance presentation and admission rates.

Hospitals have used new technological platforms to apply QI measures in overcrowded EDs at continuously increasing rates. Even in the early 2000's these platforms suggested great strides in the ability for ED staff to identify and predict overcrowding events. Some of the earlier research identified an Emergency Department Work Index (EDWI) functioning as a summary of distinguished objective standards to control patient overcrowding (Bernstein et al., 2003). The EDWI considers models for assessing patients in triage according to severity of illness or injury, the number of physicians available during influxes of patients seeking emergency care, the number of treatment areas, and the number of already admitted patients.

With the advent of computerized workspaces, mobile devices, and data sharing capabilities such programs can provide real-time updates to ED staff. A more recent prospective analysis of an electronic hands-free tool found that the simple measure of introducing a mobile admissions tracking device was perceived by 93 percent of medical residents to be more efficient than any other contemporary strategy (Gonzalo et al., 2014).

Real-time tracking of patient overcrowding greatly increases patient flow through fast track triage (Grouse et al., 2014). Alternatives triage tracks available to non-urgent patients and patients with low-complexity emergencies assist in preventing bottlenecks. Adding a physician and nurse supplementary team to the triage process reduced delays and left-without-being-seen rates without an increased number of return visits (Cheng et al., 2013). One survey study identified that 70 percent of academic hospitals in the US had implemented some form of vertical patient flow (Liu et al., 2013). However, a significant barrier to implementing this QI measure was the coordination of inpatient boarding.

Vertical patient flows and alternate triage teams were effective at reducing ED overcrowding (Woods, Reintjes, & Nagy, 2014). Triage teams should have staffing arrangements in order of seniority from a senior hospital leader, an ED physician, an ED nurse, ED support staff, and an inpatient-admitting physician. While not all ED staff will need to rely on this type of staffing coordination structure, vertical patient flow has a positive impact in areas where non-urgent, low-acuity patients seeking primary care services are commonplace.

Other QI measures proven effective at reducing ED wait times include: decrease ambulance diversion (Delgado et al., 2013), increasing the number of holding units for patients waiting to be admitted, improve lab turnaround times, smooth elective surgery caseloads, and implement regional EMS cooperative agreements using Six Sigma methods (Owad et al., 2013). Alternatively, adding a complaint box to the discharge process could bolster an Ed's quality of customer care (Griffey & Bohan, 2006). Programs in continuing education also have a strong correlation with improvements in the quality of service received by patients in an ED (Boudreaux, Cruz, & Baumann, 2006; Francis et al., 2008). Moreover, improvements in the triage process could very well extend into treatment programs requiring more extensive care to treat illnesses or injuries (Finn et al., 2013). Paramedics tasked with determining which types of patients could be safely identified, and managed without presenting to the ED. The Urgent Matters program makes use of collaborative learning networks, national conferences, e- newsletters, online seminars, best practice tool kits, and social media (McClelland et al., 2011). QI measures such as those mentioned above increase the likelihood of hospitals achieving benchmark goals of wait times less than four hours,

Benchmarking Tools for Decreasing ED Waiting Times

Recent studies highlighted the importance of addressing how hospitals use different triage systems for categorizing patients according to the severity of their illnesses or injuries (Green et al., 2014; Mullan et al., 2014; Schaaf et al., 2014; Storm-Versloot et al., 2014). The use of raw data to measure ED performance in developing tools for benchmarking ED waiting times provides misleading results (Green et al., 2014). Raw data cannot entirely account for differences in ED waiting times because of observed differences in patients and in hospitals. However, differences in practices and protocols have effects on how ED staff record times of arrival, admission, and discharge (Green et al., 2014). Long patient queues emerge when demand exceeds capacity, though no real consensus exists on the definition of patient overcrowding (Green et al., 2014). While patient overcrowding can result from the number, urgency or complexity of patients arriving at an ED, the lack of bed availability is one probable cause. ED staff does not receive consistent training how they can streamline admissions procedures to reduce patient overcrowding during the triage process (Green et al., 2014). The overall performance of a public hospital that frequently experiences the problem of patient overcrowding depends on how ED staff categorizes patients in triage. Accurate assignment of triage patients improves the delivery of health care services.

Some triage systems have more predictive value than others do, though most systems often work poorly in hospitals with limited resources (Mullan et al., 2014). Two recent studies argued for the use of a Manchester Triage System (MTS) to improve efficiency and quality of care for patients (Schaaf et al., 2014; Storm-Versloot et al., 2014). Patient satisfaction based on perceptions of receiving quality care at an ED is now more important as a concept for assessing the effectiveness of QI strategies (Storm-Versloot et al., 2014). Patient satisfaction also depended upon the number of patients concentrated in an ED at a single time and the amount of available ED staff (Schaaf et al., 2014). A Manchester Triage System may improve patient flow for researchers to map results correctly after performing a simulation run. Similar QI strategies may lead to a reduction in waiting times as the result of implementing a standardized triage system that requires frequent monitoring.

Improving patient flow remains an essential component for developing benchmark tools useful for reducing wait times to a maximum of four hours (Vezyridis & Timmons, 2014).

Clinical, organizational, and spatial issues are critical factors along with the experiences and attitudes among ED staff. Establishing a maximum waiting time of four hours helps regulate the individual and collective timescales of work in the health care industry by categorizing the work performed by different units and workspaces within an ED (Vezyridis & Timmons, 2014).

Maximum waiting times increase efficiency, clinical performance, and patient throughput measures, though they pose disruptions on established professional hierarchies and lead to the development of new professional roles (Vezyridis & Timmons, 2014). Hospitals that implement the proper benchmarking tools for setting a maximum waiting time of four hours in an ED provide more backing for patient tracking, better awareness of time constraints, and real-time management of patients by ED staff (Vezyridis & Timmons, 2014). Benchmarking tools may also further highlight the dynamic relationships between the social and technical elements of working in an ED.

Setting a maximum waiting time of four hours may place added pressure on some ED staff, leading to valid concerns about relationships between patients and staff. Hence, benchmarking tools to decrease ED waiting times to a maximum of four hours requires future research placing an emphasis on how such tools affect the experiences of both ED staff and patients. Patient satisfaction depends on the delivery of quality care by nurse practitioners, as this position is part of a reformative model in the health care industry that affects the health outcomes of patients. However, a significant gap in the research is present that addresses the effects of benchmarking tools on cost, quality of care, and patient satisfaction (Jennings et al., 2015). Nurse practitioners have a role to play in establishing benchmarking tools for improving the quality of care, though the type of care that patients receive in an ED depends on a combination of follow-up research on health outcomes (Jennings et al., 2015). Benchmarking tools may also need to account for the provision of educational opportunities in patients by having ED staff explain the purpose of a waiting list and explaining some of the reasons for overcrowding (Messina et al., 2015; Obamiro, 2013). Both waiting times and having enough information may help increase patient satisfaction.

Lean Thinking Principles

Benchmarking tools depend on the use of lean thinking principles that may help reduce ED overcrowding, delays, cost containment, and patient satisfaction (Chan et al., 2014; Holden, 2011; Majidi et al., 2014; Martens et al., 2014). An earlier study identified how changes in structure and process involving the use of new technologies, communication systems, staffing changes, and the reorganization of physical space affect the quality of care that patients receive (Holden, 2011). Lean thinking principles may aid public hospitals in the Detroit metropolitan area to decrease ED waiting times while they may also decrease the number of LWBS and LAMA patients. However, many questions remain about the effect of lean thinking principles on the health outcomes of patients who receive care in an ED (Holden, 2011). Lean thinking principles also have implications for an entire health care system in this regard.

Lean thinking principles improve patient flow in an ED as much as they also enhance the quality of emergency care and patient satisfaction. As such, lean thinking principles reduce waiting times in triage and consultation while they also reduce waiting times for results in laboratory and radiological work and the total time between admissions and discharge (Chan et al., 2014). However, as one recent study suggested, hospitals may need to introduce lean thinking principles in phases through an integrative process combining elements of lean thinking principles and Six Sigma management (Martens et al., 2014). A "Lean Six Sigma" methodology would consider the use of phases for assessment, improvement, and sustainability for improving health outcomes and increasing patient satisfaction (Martens et al., 2014). An assessment phase is important for recognizing the effects of patient overcrowding in different hospitals located in the Detroit metropolitan area so that researchers may draw proper comparisons and contrasts as well as develop adequate tools for best practices and changing infrastructure. Secondly, an improvement phase would optimize paths and best practice tools implemented by an ED at each hospital in the Detroit metropolitan area (Martens et al., 2014). The improvement phase would necessarily involve training ED staff on new processes and support for patients.

Finally, a phase for providing sustainability in positive health outcomes of patients would include recognizing support along with proper tools and metrics for measuring patient satisfaction (Martens et al., 2014). The study by Martens and colleagues (2014) suggests that while a Lean Six Sigma methodology has a clear structure, the process is not rigid in its application, and many different hospitals within a metropolitan area have the possibility of using lean thinking procedures in different ways. Standardization of lean thinking principles is not possible for all hospitals, and each hospital in the Detroit metropolitan area would need to implement tools and principles that fit their unique case.

Financial Implications

While the adverse clinical outcomes linked to patient overcrowding have been well established, it is likely the financial burden of this problem will encourage positive change (Holden, 2011). In their commentary on the economic framework of EDs, Becker and Friedman (2013) looked at the financial realities of the patient overcrowding debate. They argued that when hospitals decrease waiting times through admission of uninsured patients and direct ED treatments they incur an increased burden of cost (Becker & Friedman, 2013). A decrease in overcrowding has been shown to be financially beneficial, however. Pines and colleagues (2011) reviewed the financial implications of reducing ED boarding on gross hospital revenue. The findings indicated that while non-ED admissions generated more revenue than ED admissions, a one-hour reduction in ED boarding time could result in as much as $4,000 of additional daily revenue. Thus, ED reduction time is a financially attractive strategy (Pines et al., 2011). The findings have a direct correlation to primary care as a major reason for non- urgent patients to seek care at an ED. Song and colleagues (2013) tracked a mobile health clinic in an urban area and found that the primary care benefits community residents gained from the mobile clinic could result in decreases in the relative risk of high-acuity events such as myocardial infarctions.

The intended purpose of legislative measures to increase primary health care access is generally aimed at decreasing the national burden of rising health care costs. The ethical considerations of such measures also have a major impact on the ED (Marco et al., 2012).

Health care reform measures in Massachusetts led to a small but significant decrease in the rate of low-acuity visits by low income, uninsured patients (Smulowitz et al., 2011). Efforts to limit state payment of Medicaid benefits for frequent or unnecessary ED visits are simply an indicator that many regions in the state have poor access to primary care services.

Summary of Major Contributions from Key Research Studies

Certain contributions to the understanding of ED overcrowding have helped placed the issue on the national stage as new legislative measures promise increased affordability and access to health insurance. Certainly, this topic is of major concern to the millions of ED patients waiting in line, yet key contributors have translated that concern into an important discussion on health insurance, primary care access, and QI of health systems. The study by Hoot and Aronsky (2008) guided the literature review to develop a conceptual framework was laid out that identified the causative aspects of ED overcrowding through Input-Throughput-Output factors. This conceptual framework allowed them to identify four primary issues that are directly correlated to patient overcrowding: adverse clinical outcomes from both ED patients and admitted inpatients, reduced quality of care including delays in treatment and transport, impaired access to ED services due to ambulance diversion and patient elopement, and provider losses.

QI measures can be implemented in thanks to the identification of such specific and correlated outcomes. Bernstein and colleagues (2009) used the Institute of Medicine's six domains of quality care to further identify which QI measures showed growth potential. The domains of safety, patient-centeredness, timeliness, efficiency, effectiveness, and equity have been used as metrics in their own right, and this study as well as others have identified safety and timeliness as the primary factors of quality care that are not being met (Bernstein et al., 2009).

Summary of the Current Status of the Problem
in Light of Recent Research

QI measures have shown significant worth in the ED, and current QI measures such as mobile admitting platforms, overcrowding alert systems, and real-time coordination across regional EDs will likely play a major role in the reduction of patient overcrowding. Stone and colleagues (2013) showed impressive work with their inquiry into non-urgent ED patients. This study was coupled to an ED medical screening exam with a medical referral system linking non- urgent ED patients to a local clinic (Stone et al, 2013). Non-urgent patients deemed appropriate for referral were satisfied with the screening process, 85 percent elected to receive care at the clinic that day (Stone et al., 2013). Becker and Friedman (2013) were some of the first to identify hospital value-based purchasing initiatives as they relate to ED overcrowding. They laid out an argument that showed the significant financial disincentives hospitals experience in their task of decreasing patient overcrowding. While overcrowding is certainly tied to derogatory health outcomes, hospitals take on a heavy burden of increased cost due to expensive ED treatments and uninsured hospital admissions (Becker & Friedman, 2013). Continued looks into the financial and QI aspects of patient overcrowding may be the best approaches to reducing this problem.

Possible Directions for Future Research

Future research should focus on implementing and studying QI strategies, especially vertical integration of the triage process, mobile platforms for patient care and admissions, and tracking of financial incentives to care provision. Future research should also focus on increasing the data sets of healthcare systems. Kellerman and Weinick (2012) were able to identify significant barriers to primary care based on regional Medicaid data. As QI measures within health systems rely on electronic record keeping, research on patient overcrowding in an ED benefits from larger and more in-depth data sets, and collaboration should take place with economics, human resources, and business management researchers.

CHAPTER 3
Methodology

This chapter highlights the methodology designed to answer the research questions proposed in the Chapter 1. Analyzing the current state of ED overcrowding in Detroit hospitals, along with the effects of primary care accessibility and health insurance availability, depends on the use of a mixed methods methodology (Creswell, Klassen, Clark, & Smith, 2011). The chapter describes the quantitative and qualitative measures used to analyze ED overcrowding at hospitals in the Detroit metropolitan area. The measures also lead to an analysis of population selection to inform the intended outcomes of those research questions.

Mixed methods research in the health sciences aims to develop new methodologies for improving the quality and magnitude of data (Creswell et al., 2011). Mixed methods research also promotes diversity in methods that reflect the nature of problems facing public health. A substantial amount of influence in mixed methods research draws from the acceptance of qualitative research in the social sciences, the formation of interdisciplinary teams, and the use of approaches from multiple angles to investigate problems in public health (Creswell et al., 2011). Current use of mixed methods research applies to past research in specializations of the public health industry, with settings varying from clinics and hospitals to social contexts of daily activities and personal relationships among patients and health professionals (Creswell et al., 2011). The National Institute of Health (NIH) has a growing interest in the use of mixed methods research since 1996, with support from the National Institute of Mental Health (NIMH), the National Institute of Nursing Research (NINR), and the National Cancer Institute (NCI; Creswell et al., 2011). However, despite the growing interest and institutional support for mixed methods research, new guidelines are necessary for ensuring "best practices" apply to scientific researchers who require funding for aiding reviewers in assessing the quality of this methodology (Creswell et al., 2011). Some of the recommendations for using mixed methods research are outdated and are not in line with current knowledge as it applies to real-world health problems that require the use of mixed methods.

Some of the qualitative methods drawing from social sciences include approaches such as in-depth interviews, field observations, case studies to understand the range of unique experiences, the amount of involvement in interventions for improving the quality of public health systems, and the types of barriers and promoters of successful treatment (Creswell et al., 2011). Qualitative methods also combine the use of clinical trials, surveys of attitudes and beliefs, and epidemiological research to understand the range of problems in a public health system. More specifically, qualitative methods help researchers identify key processes as they emerge from the data over time, provide detailed information settings and context, and emphasize the use of interview data from participants through quotes (Creswell et al., 2011).

When other measures are not available, qualitative methods make data collection easier as it provides researchers with tools for understanding concepts as they emerged from data (Creswell et al., 2012). Aside from the use of case studies, other qualitative approaches include grounded theory, ethnography, and phenomenology (Creswell et al., 2012). While grounded theory emphasizes that a theory emerging from the data, ethnography emphasizes detailed observations of setting and location while phenomenology emphasizes patterns in the lived experience of all participants in a study.

On the other hand, quantitative research methods are more typical of deductive analyses of hard data when the goal is to test theories and hypotheses by gathering descriptive information and examining relationships among variables (Creswell et al., 2011). Quantitative research methods often measure and yield numeric data analyzed to produce statistical information. More specifically, quantitative data provide empirical evidence to help establish a probability of cause and effect, promote efficiency in data collection techniques, promote the greater likelihood that future studies can replicate the methods used in prior studies, generalize to a larger population, provide distinct information for comparing groups, and provide insights into a broad range of experiences (Creswell et al., 2011). In the health sciences, quantitative research typically involves the use of descriptive surveys, observational studies, case-control series, randomized clinical trials (RCTs), and time-series designs occur at the observational level with hypotheses explaining those observations and predictions for data collection while they also lend to the verification of measurements and findings.

Qualitative measures occur at the phenomenological level in consideration of the following: assumptions of qualitative approaches within one qualitative genre (trustworthiness), ethical considerations, choice of overall design, rationale behind the selection of measures used for data collection, and a realistic projection of the need for resources to reduce ED overcrowding. The ethical impetus for the study is trustworthiness and its applicability to QI research. Trustworthiness provides a needed foundation for ensuring that the methodology used is reliable and valid for when accounting for the clarity and accuracy of results.

Trustworthiness is necessary when conducting healthcare-based QI research. Qualitative measures for data collection depend highly on trustworthiness to analyze findings for reliability, validity, and objectivity. Some methodological practices are especially useful to ensure the trustworthiness of the data collected, including: triangulation, searching for evidence that disproves or challenges the results of previous studies, engaging in reflexivity, member checking, prolonged engagement in the field, collaboration, developing an audit trail, and participant debriefing (Marshall & Rossman, 2010). An Institutional Review Board (IRB) reviewed the proposed study for ethical considerations and did not grant approval for conducting research until both quantitative and qualitative measures were ensured.

Organization of the Remainder of the Chapter

The rest of the methodology is organized as follows:

1. Research Questions
2. Research Design
    a. Qualitative Methods
    b. Quantitative Methods
    c. Overview of the Quality Systems Design Used in this Study
3. Population and Sample
4. Selection of Participants
5. Instrumentation
6. Procedures
7. Data Collection
8. Data Analysis
9. Reliability and Validity

Research Questions

Two primary research questions informed this study. Both are based on the overarching goal of exploring the relationship between ED overcrowding and poor health outcomes. In light of recent economic troubles in the Detroit metropolitan area this study will seek to answer:

1. What is the current state of patient overcrowding in the emergency departments of public hospitals in Detroit, Michigan?

2. How does ED overcrowding affect the health outcomes of patients who must wait in excess of six hours to receive care?

Research Design

Within the research, methodologies for a healthcare-based QI research study a number of QI-specific and scientifically general items. Qualitative measures form the basis of this study while quantitative measures aid in providing detail. The site selection, population selection, and sampling must be done in a way that informs the subjective intentions of the hypothesis and the objective facts of the research questions. Ethical considerations follow, as well as the researcher's role within the study, and the ways in which the researcher's role may affect the overall outcome of the qualitative and quantitative segments of the study. This is most important when considering the qualitative segment.

The data collection methods must be organized and, again, informed by the primary research questions. A data analysis strategy must be laid out in order to organize the resulting information gained from the two sides of the study, which relates most importantly to the quantitative segment. A management plan must encompass the study, and there should always be a focus on reliability and validity at each step in the analysis of data.

Healthcare-based QI strategies have gained in popularity over the past decade. This is largely due to the significance of operations and quality interventions found in previous QI implementations. Research studies based in QI have also showed success when both quantitative and qualitative methods are used in a mixed-methods approach. The United States National Institute of Health (NIH) Office of Behavioral and Social Science Research commissioned a report defining best practices in mixed methods research that argues for rigorous methodology.

Their recommendations include research that explores the research questions with a multifaceted and external perspective, a quantitative assessment of large data sets, a qualitative component that explores the meaning and understanding of constructs, a methodology that joins multiple methods in a harmonious and reinforcing way, and the joining of findings to overall philosophical and theoretical understandings (Creswell et al., 2011). A strong methodology incorporates these items, while always referring back to the primary research questions.

Research with a QI focus follows much of the same path that all other academic research follows. It does require, however, a mixed-methods approach in order to validate the philosophical and theoretical foundations upon which the QI strategies were built. Research itself is a systematic way of exploring and answering problems within the world (Reaves, 1992). QI research is an applied version of such inquiry. Applied research is any research that has as a primary goal the intention to solve real-world problems, or simply to make real-time decisions in a practical manner. Evaluation research is generally focused on the ongoing evaluation of a program that has been implemented, or could be implemented (Reaves, 1992). Evaluation research bids summative evaluations and formative evaluations against each other, while also gauging the impact versus the process of the program in question.

In this research methodology, the focus will heavily be on formative evaluation in which the intention is to diagnose specific areas of the current healthcare system in the Detroit Metropolitan area as it relates to ED overcrowding. It will also have an impact evaluation focus in which quantitative and qualitative data is used to identify specific problems within the program in question. The use of applied research method-ologies does require caution. It is easy to lose control over any experimental controls imposed on such a broad population, the qualitative components may precipitate adverse reactions in the study participants, and the quantitative component brings about a breadth of data that must be properly managed and cross-referenced (Reaves, 1992). In order to address these potential issues, a firm grasp of the flow of general science is maintained. From description of the problem to predictions regarding the outcome of the data collected, and from explanatory models to experimentally, imposed controls the subjective and objective predispositions must always take into consideration the final goal of science: "to control something is to make things tend to happen in a certain way" (Reaves, 1992, p. 23). In doing this any potential adverse reaction to the study will be deflected.

This research methodology relates, at all times, to the two primary research questions.

Namely, the internal causative factors associated with increased ED overcrowding, and the external causative factors of primary health care access and health insurance access in the Detroit metropolitan area will be investigated. The research design itself made use of quantitative and qualitative factors in a recip-rocal way. The quantitative component involves the use of large healthcare data sets from three Detroit metropolitan and Michigan state organizations. The primary observation, as mentioned above, focused on the prevalence of primary care access, health insurance availability, and the causative relationship with ED overcrowding.

The main hypothesis is that decreased primary care access and decreased health insurance availability in the Detroit metropolitan area are directly proportional to ED overcrowding. A null hypothesis is that decreased access to primary care access and decreased health insurance availability in the Detroit metropolitan has no effect on the status of ED overcrowding. Mixed methods research aided in providing internal validity and in verifying the findings of this study.

A mixed methods research approach on this scale does not necessitate a robust, or even large, team of researchers, but it does necessitate similar precautions that would be made if such a study was to be incorporated on a larger scale (Creswell et al., 2011). The primary focus within mixed methods research depends on the significance of the research questions. The nature of those questions must remain ambivalent to the preliminary data, as well as to conclusions made after conducting the study. A successful mixed methods approach that uses a research team must have a broad perspective on how to integrate different methodologies while research teams must also have an ability to support and acknowledge the contributions of all team members (Creswell et al., 2011, p. 12). Research teams that used a mixed methods approach should also maintain an effort sustain dialogue about issues when working in collaboration, a sensitivity to workloads of team members that may pose challenges to working on the project, and support for educating team members in different methodologies when needed" (Creswell et al., 2011, p. 12). Similarly, without a large team the intended consequences of the mixed methods approach are magnified on the few conducting the study. In that manner, the use of a linear mixed methods research structure will be used in this research.

The expertise of the thesis board will be used as well as contemporary doctoral students and other researchers who will inform decisions made within the study. This will allow differing perspectives and differing levels of expertise to guide potential problems as the methodology is unrolled.

Qualitative Methods

In this study, qualitative methods rely heavily on the quantitative data gained in the procedures detailed below to provide support for the main hypothesis that decreased access to primary care access and decreased health insurance availability in the Detroit metropolitan area have a strong correlation to ED overcrowding. Conceptual frameworks developed from the use of qualitative research methods for a QI-oriented research study in the health sciences must have a solid rationale (Marshall & Rossman, 2011). Research questions should have clear links to the theoretical hypothesis that the health care system in the United States faces significant and varied impacts based socioeconomic classifications and legislative policies.

Marshall and Rossman (2011) recommended that qualitative methodology follow six topics: the assumptions of qualitative approaches within one qualitative genre (phenomenological), the trustworthiness of the overall methodology, considerations for ethical issues, the choice of the overall design, the rationale behind the selection of specific data collection measurements, and a realistic projection of the resource needs. A phenomenological approach with an emphasis on in-depth interviews with focus seeks to develop a direct understanding of the direct lived experiences as articulated by Detroit metropolitan residents and health professionals.

Phenomenological Research

Qualitative methods employed phenomenological research for interviewing participants via in-depth focus groups to collect data. Phenomenological research for this study consisted of an in-depth interviewing technique grounded in the philosophy of phenomenology (Marshall & Rossman, 2011). Lived experiences and the ways that participants understand those experiences helps develop a worldview and thus a theoretical construct. Phenomenological research assumes that each lived experience is both shared and has a "structure and essence" that provides a narrative framework for collecting and analyzing data (Marshall & Rossman, 2011, p. 148).

Prior to conducting interviews that use phenomenological research methods, researchers may need to write of their own experiences to rid of any possible bias against participants. Here, researchers engage in what is commonly known as *epoché*, or a period of self-examination to gain clarity about preconceptions (Marshall & Rossman, 2011, p. 148). After the *epoché*, researchers practice *phenomenological reduction* to identify the essence of a studied phenomenon for categorizing data by theme (Marshall & Rossman, 2011). Finally, researchers using a phenomenological methodology practice a *structural synthesis* that involves exploring all possible meanings and perspectives as they lead to a description of an essence and its structure.

In-Depth Focus Groups

Interviews with focus groups, however, uses a slightly different methodology than phenomenology, as the approach has its roots in marketing research but was widely adapted to include social science and applied research (Marshall & Rossman, 2011, p. 149). Most in-depth focus groups contain between four to twelve individuals who have no prior personal knowledge of another, and were selected to participate in a study because of demonstrating similar characteristics based on the research questions. Interviewers may create supportive environments by asking focused questions that promote discussion among participants who may express diametrically opposed viewpoints (Marshall & Rossman, 2011). Researchers may conduct multiple interviews with focus groups, though researchers may also conduct follow-up interviews with specific individuals who participated in a focus group to gain further insight. A unique advantage to using in-depth focus groups is that, because of continued technological developments, no physical presence in a room is necessary. Researchers have the authority to conduct in-depth focus entirely in a "virtual" setting not limited by time or location. For this study, conducting interviews with doctors may prove difficult depending if their work is necessary in locations other than the Detroit metropolitan area.

A central assumption of a methodology that uses in-depth interviews with focus groups is that individual attitudes and beliefs are socially constructed (Marshall & Rossman, 2011). Yet the questions asked by researchers who use a phenomenological approach to in-depth interviews with focus group promote the expression of diverse viewpoints within a supportive environment. Participants feel comfortable expressing their viewpoints because the environment provides a more natural and relaxed setting than one-on-one interviews might (Marshall & Rossman, 2011). Interviews with focus groups provide a substantial amount of assistance for researchers to gain access to important information, focusing site selection and sampling, and checking for possible conclusions by allowing interviews to explore a variety of potential issues as they emerge (Marshall & Rossman, 2011). In terms of validity, in-depth focus groups demonstrate face validity because the approach is popular.

The focus groups took place after completing the collection of quantitative data. All participants were categorized into one of five groups: socioeconomic status, health care status, primary care physician status, patients with at least three ED visits in past twelve months, and at least one admission to a hospital through an ED in the past twelve months. Each group included ten Detroit metropolitan residents. The size of each group met the minimum sample size for saturation and remained under a maximum sample size for developing a case. The study used recruited participants instead of purposeful sampling. The benefits of this approach to qualitative data collection included high data yields in a short time, wide variety of information, and quick follow-up with participants.

The limitations include trustworthiness of participants, and the interpersonal problems that may prevent overt discussions of validity. The strengths of such a mixed methods approach include the reciprocal nature of quantitative and qualitative methodology focused on a common hypothesis. The large data sets incorporated into the quantitative methodology will identify focus group participants, and in turn, the data collected from the focus group interviews will inform the validity and reliability of the quantitative data sets explored. There are limitations, however. The data analysis period will rely on an understanding of biostatistics, and the complexity of the evaluations will increase. In addition, a multidisciplinary thesis board must be readily available to steer theoretical constructs in the right direction.

Quantitative Methods

The quantitative component of this research used three electronic healthcare databases: the Greater Detroit Area Health Council (GDAHC), the Michigan Department of Community Health (MDCH), and the national reporting firm Modern Healthcare. The GDAHC supplied data for primary care utilization and patient overcrowding events in the Detroit Metropolitan area (GDAHC, 2014). The MDCH (2014) provided a database of Medicaid beneficiaries from the state of Michigan. Modern Healthcare provided a database of trends in the health insurance markets of Detroit in particular and Michigan as a whole. The internal data drawn from Modern Healthcare led to an analysis of uncommon events, incident-reporting forms, rates of infection, length of ED wait, frequency of lengthy ED wait times, expenditure reports, boarding time, and patient complaints. Database research from Modern Healthcare aided in providing tools for conducting an external analysis of specific client demographics including race/ethnicity, socioeconomic status, frequency of hospital stays, mortality, and morbidity linked to risk factors, and treatment procedures. The basic quantitative methodology follows the order of observations made about something that is unknown, hypothesizing an explanation for these observations within large data sets, predictions of the outcomes, data collection, and verification of measurements and findings. The analysis of these databases for these measurements involves the use of a correlation design. The study is correlational in that it attempts the determine the extent of the relationship between primary care access, health insurance availability, and lengthy ED waiting times as a function of measurements stated above.

Overview of the Quality Systems Design Used in this Study

Healthcare-based QI research that relies on a mixed methods approach is oriented to propose the best systems-based research claims from its data. In order to do this in a Quality Systems focus, the following steps are proposed in this methodology. The identification of Detroit EDs as an area of interest, the evaluation of existing ED and primary care processes in Detroit, the determination of potential interventions to decrease patient overcrowding, and the evaluation of the impact of these interventions in the Detroit metropolitan area. Lean Thinking and Six Sigma principles will run concurrent with these four steps. The Lean Thinking principles of identifying customer value, the identification of the value stream, and the elimination of waste will be the primary applications of the phenomenological focus group approach. The Six Sigma principles of achieving stability by predictable process results and a clear commitment to decision making will be major focuses in the application of the quantitative methodology.

Population and Sample

Detroit metropolitan residents will be the primary population focus of this research methodology. Michigan Medicaid beneficiaries will be sought, but the focus will remain on the Detroit metropolitan area. Health insurance data gathered from Modern Healthcare will also focus on this region. The samples from these data sets voluntarily co-opted into the phenomenological qualitative focus groups will be partitioned into the following ten-person groups: socioeconomic status, health care status, primary care physician status, three ED visits in last year, and admission to hospital through ED in last year.

Selection of Participants

Proper sampling within healthcare-based QI mixed methods research works to minimize sampling bias and provide validity and reliability for supporting the main hypothesis. Sampling should thus subsequently follow into data collection and data analysis. For a healthcare-based QI research, study participant selection took the form of non-probability sampling, probability sampling, systematic sampling, stratified sampling, and cluster sampling. The research methodology used probability sampling to give every resident of the Detroit metropolitan area a known probability of being selected for the sample, within the confines of the quantitative data sets garnered from the three sources previously listed.

Probability sampling is the most basic sampling technique for this research, such a simple random sample will allow for the most competent, and valid, conclusions based on the data.

Reaves (1992) underlines the importance of such sampling stating "decisions about sampling people and events are made concurrently with decisions about the specific data collection methods to be used and should be thought through in advance" (p. 105). A detailed sampling of participants enhances the reciprocal nature of this mixed methods approach.

Instrumentation

The different aspects of this mixed methods study used different forms of instrumentation, but all computer-based approaches used *Windows* platform. The quantitative component of instrumentation utilized databases from the GDAHC, the MDCH, and Modern Healthcare. The GDAHC provided data for primary care utilization and patient overcrowding events in the Detroit Metropolitan area, the MDCH provided a database of Medicaid beneficiaries from the state of Michigan, and Modern Healthcare provided a database of trends in the health insurance markets of Detroit in particular and Michigan as a whole. The statistical computing software *R* was used to organize statistical models of this data, and *Microsoft Excel* was used to organize data sets. The qualitative component of instrumentation involved the use of focus groups guided by an observational experimenter questionnaire. Interviews were recorded using a *QL Tools* audio recorder. The interviews were then transcribed verbatim.

Procedures

Healthcare-based QI research constructs must have proper procedures for measuring the variables and accounting for any correlations between them. The procedures of this study, aided by the use of mixed methods applications, focused on the organization of large data sets from the GDAHC, the MDCH, and Modern Healthcare. As the combination of these data sets have a high degree of reliability, the procedures for data collection and analysis have strong links to proper sampling techniques to enhance the validity and reliability of the research claims. In their guide to using data as a QI tool, the fundamentals of data measurement procedures that are accessible should be used more heavily in practice (Victorian Quality Council [VQC], 2008). The steps outlined in this methodology adhere that statement as a procedural tool for providing reliable and valid conclusions that rely heavily on proper data management.

According to the Victorian Quality Council (2008), nine domains of health system performance are important to consider for proper data measurements. Quality improvement depends on the criteria of effectiveness, appropriateness, safety, efficiency responsiveness, accessibility, continuity, capability, and sustainability. Both effectiveness and appropriateness help researchers in the health sciences evaluate for care as well as interventions or actions for achieving desired outcomes, though appropriateness is slightly different in that this criterion for quality improvement emphasizes the needs of clients based on established standards (VQC, 2008). The criteria of effectiveness and safety involve researchers identifying reports of morbidity and mortality.

The criterion of appropriateness also helps researchers identify service utilization data and audit information against international standards based on evidence-based guidelines (VQC, 2008). Service utilization data is also useful for researchers to evaluate the quality criteria of efficiency, responsiveness, and accessibility while those three criteria also help researchers in the health sciences evaluate complaints from patients, failure-to-attend rates and, in relation to this study, waiting times. (VQC, 2008). Along with waiting times, the criterion of efficiency aids researchers in audits of equipment and resources usage.

The criterion of safety involves the avoidance or reduction to acceptable limits of actual or potential harm from health care management or the health care environment where patients receive services (VQC, 2008). More specifically, safety refers to the avoidance or reduction of actual or perceived harm in health care management. Accreditation reports aid researchers in evaluating this measure for quality improvement as these types of reports also apply to the criteria of capability and sustainability, though the criterion of capability runs in conjunction with that of continuity in reference to preventing adverse health outcomes while also reducing ED waiting times (VQC, 2008). Sustainability is a highly important criterion that aids researchers in identifying measurements for quality improvement by noting any integration with data systems as well as business plans and resource allocation (VQC, 2008). Here, sustainability applies to how reductions in ED wait times affect health outcomes in patients within the context of an entire health care system. Sustainability holds importance for researchers in the health sciences to analyze the capacity for a health care system to provide infrastructure in terms of workforce, facilities, equipment, and use of innovative technologies to provide for urgent needs.

An evaluation of quality improvement processes in the health sciences involves a five- stage process—project identification, diagnosis, intervention, impact, and sustained improvements—in a continuous cycle (NSW Health, Department 2001). Project definition is important for researchers in the health sciences for knowing what they want to accomplish and who to involve in the data collection process (NSW Health Department, 2001). Diagnosis refers to establishing the full extent of a problem as well as to knowing what types of changes will most likely lead towards improvements and how to measure them. Interventions refer to implementing the changes identified in the previous phase while impact involves measuring and recording the effects of changes to a quality improvement process (NSW Health Department, 2001). Finally, the process of sustained improvements refers to researchers in the health sciences developing an ongoing system for monitoring and planning for future improvements.

Evaluations of quality improvement processes also involve research in the health sciences using a cycle of planning, doing, studying, and acting with two central components of asking three fundamental questions in any order and applying a number of tests to determine what changes will lead to significant improvements (NSW Health Department, 2001). One noted distinction to make for researchers in the health sciences is that models for quality improvement to decrease ED waiting times emphasizes changes made to the health care system and not, in all cases, improved health outcomes for patients (NSW Health Department, 2001).

Due to the complexity of healthcare systems, and the increased digitization of healthcare data, proper QI procedures may be the future of increased efficiency within the American healthcare system. This methodology proposes data collection procedures that will rely on three databases described below. The use of three databases will act in a reciprocal manner, and only once proper data collection and analysis procedures are completed qualitative focus groups will follow. These focus groups will make use of local, regional, and national procedures for the safe, effective, reliable, and valid collection of qualitative data.

Data Collection

Mixed methods research on this level, incorporating healthcare-based QI in a qualitative and quantitative manner, is strongest when experienced researchers in a linear structure oversee them. Yet, it is a necessary requirement of the researcher in question to be able to make use of large data sets as healthcare data becomes increasingly digitized and stored in electronic formats. Any mixed methods approach that uses such large data sets and links quantitative findings to qualitative findings will require computer software programs and an understanding of statistical interpretations. Electronic healthcare-oriented databases will be used from three organizations: the Greater Detroit Area Health Council (GDAHC), the Michigan Department of Community Health (MDCH), and the national reporting firm Modern Healthcare.

The GDAHC has a mission to "improve the health and well-being of people living in southwest Michigan by solving health problems that can be addressed only through multi-sector collaboration" (GDAHC 2014, p. 1). This research methodology proposes the utilization of GDAHC primary care and ED reported statistics from the primary healthcare centers in this region. The GDAHC is targeted for this data collection due to their organization of a large group of Detroit metropolitan hospitals, non-profit organizations linked to Detroit healthcare, and independent benefactors focused on increasing the use of electronic databases for healthcare, and in this case healthcare-based QI, purposes.

The MDCH has a mission to "protect, preserve, and promote the health and safety of the people of Michigan with particular attention to providing for the needs of vulnerable and under- served populations" (MDCH, 2014, p. 1). The MDCH also reports health statistics for this region and is primarily responsible for the oversight of Michigan's Medicaid program. The utilization of Medicaid statistics within the Detroit area will help inform research inquiry into the accessibility of health insurance in the area. Currently, the MDCH reports that the total Medicaid caseload for Michigan is over 1.7 million people, a record high, with much of those people concentrated in Detroit, and nearly one-third of Michigan Medicaid beneficiaries are not enrolled in managed care, necessitating a look at ED utilization by such beneficiaries for primary care purposes. Finally, Modern Healthcare's databases of health insurance markets will be used to correlate ED use with Medicaid availability, and private health insurance availability.

The qualitative component of this methodology will be informed by the resulting data collected in the quantitative component. Collection of qualitative data will take place in the form of focus groups conducted by the primary researcher in a Detroit area hospital, and focus group participants will be voluntarily co-opted from the samples of quantitative data.

Data Analysis

Mixed methods data analysis helps researchers in the health sciences synthesize principles of quantitative and qualitative research measurements. Any form of scientific inquiry makes use of a general understanding of measurement by noting the relationship between a predefined set of concepts and using those them in a specific research context. Reaves (1992) used the analogy of a ruler to define the objective of scientific inquiry by arguing that while a ruler identifies the relationship between length and a system of labels, the units of length are simply pre-arranged agreements by which researchers conduct an empirical analysis of length. In healthcare-based mixed methods research on quality improvement, a main of conducting an empirical analysis is to develop constructs or abstract concepts of phenomenon that are not directly observed (Reaves, 1992). The conceptual variables derived from an empirical analysis has similarities with grounded theory, and provide a foundation for data collection and analysis for building theoretical propositions to either support or reject the main hypothesis.

Nominal Measurements

In mixed methods research, four levels of measurement aid in the development of objective standards and theoretical propositions derived from qualitative and quantitative aspects. These four levels of measurement include nominal measurement, ordinal measurement, interval measurement, and ratio measurement. Nominal measurement is the use of symbols for specific properties to differentiate between items or subjects based only on their names or associated categories as well as on other qualitative characteristics (Reaves, 1992). While nominal measurements may lead to the discovery of an exception to classification as a sign of progress and improvement, nominal measurements may also use numbers to represent variables though the numbers do not need to have a significant relationship (Reaves, 1992). Examples of classifications for nominal measurements include gender, nationality, ethnicity, language, and biological species. Measuring the central tendency in nominal measurements refers to the mode, or the most common item, found in the data (Reaves, 1992). Using the median to measure central tendency in nominal measurements is counterproductive since nominal measurements do not use a ranking system.

In this study, the nominal measurements analyzed had a main construct of access to primary patients enrolled in Medicaid who use an ED as a source of primary care. In addition, Patients not enrolled in Medicaid who uses an ED as a source of primary care, patients with private insurance who use an ED as a source of primary care, and patients without insurance who use an ED as a source of primary care holders. These categories of patients aided in the development of nominal constructs for analyzing the effects of patient overcrowding on the effects of health outcomes in patients in cases where they had to wait for more than six hours until they received care.

Ordinal Measurements

Ordinal measurements are different from nominal measurements because they provide ranking system for sorted data (Reaves, 1992). However, ordinal measurements do not allow for a relative degree of difference between data sets. In ordinal measurements, dichotomous data in health sciences would a ranking system for "sick" versus "healthy" in measuring the health outcomes of patients who waited more than six hours in an ED at hospitals located in the Detroit metropolitan area. Conversely, non-dichotomous data consist of a spectrum of values when measuring opinions (Reaves, 1992). Non-dichotomous data pertain to the use of both qualitative and quantitative research methods in refer to how, on the one hand, qualitative data indicate subjective measurements of health care standards among patients and health professionals while, on the other hand, quantitative measures allow researchers to more easily arrange the data in aggregate form. In terms of central tendency, a notable difference between ordinal and nominal measurements is that the former allows researchers to use the median and mode but not the mean. The mean does not have validity in ordinal measurements though they have their use for improving how researchers in the health sciences operationalize variables in questionnaires.

Using the median in ordinal measurements provides researchers with opportunities for finding a middle ground for the range of data collected from patients and health professionals regarding their interpretations of how, for instance, quality improvements can reduce patient overcrowding in hospitals located in the Detroit metropolitan area. The ordinal aspect of this data analysis applied a scale for measuring the level of access to primary care on a regular basis among patients who made frequent visits to an ED and the level of health insurance that patients have when making frequent visits to an ED as a regular source of primary care. Both of those ordinal measurements provided a model for noting the possible causes of patient overcrowding.

Interval Measurements

Unlike ordinal measurements, interval measurements categorize the data and allow for a degree of difference between items and categories. However, interval measurements do not allow for the calculation of ratios between quantitative data. This study analyzed the links to equal interval measurements to determine a shared qualitative distance between the four patient categories (Reaves, 1992). Ratio measurements are equal interval measurements that have a true zero value that is arbitrarily defined (Reaves, 1992). For this study, zero value is the interval type between residents in the Detroit metropolitan area without health insurance but who use an ED as a regular source of accessing primary care and residents in the Detroit metropolitan area who have either private insurance or Medicaid who also use an ED as a regular source of accessing primary care.

Central tendency in interval measurements involve the use of mode, median, and mean while measuring statistical information in this context includes range and standard deviation (Reaves, 1992). Both central tendency and measuring statistical information help to define some elements about the causes of patient overcrowding in this study. However, researchers in the health sciences should caution that while the ratio of differences between interval measurements have a unique meaning, the mean of all interval measurements denotes a possible causal relation between variables.

Ratio Measurements

Ratio measurements derive their name from how researchers estimate the ratio between a magnitude of aggregate data and the magnitude of individual and similar data (Reaves, 1992).

Ratio measurements have similar meaning to interval measurements in that both have a zero- value, though zero-values in ratio measurements are not arbitrary as they are in interval measurements. Ratio measurements are clearly quantitative in how they describe differences in terms of "how much" or "how long." Measurements of magnitude indicate noticeable differences from one point to another. Examples of ratio measurements use quantitative data of mass, length, and duration.

For this study, duration of ED waiting times is critical for measuring the differences of experiences between patients at hospitals located in the Detroit metropolitan area. Central tendency in ratio measurements allows the use of geometric and harmonic mean along with the mode, median, and mean. Ratio measurements allow for all statistical measurements because of their quantitative nature via the use of mathematics to define a range of data that researchers can group into categories with meaning. Moreover, range and standard deviation allow for measuring the dispersion of statistical information in ratio measurements.

The Use of Statistical Data to Measure Qualitative Scales

Nominal, ordinal, equal interval and ratio measurements must be described with statistical means. The quantitative component of this mixed methods healthcare-based QI study generated a considerable amount of statistical data partitioning a scale of patients with and without health insurance in relation to behaviors of seeking regular access to primary care.

Reaves (1992) defined a statistic as a number calculated by applying some mathematical procedure to a group of other numbers. Statistics have links to frequencies, or the number of data points that fall into each category of some measurement scheme. Measurements can be identified as:

True value + Irrelevant values + Random Error = Measurement

In this study, data analysis identified the scale of health insurance as related to the frequency of visits to an ED, and by patients without regular access to primary care. Data analysis also identified a frequency distribution by which all points on the scale were described as a percentage. This percentage was then correlated was with a central tendency. The central tendency identified the majority of Detroit metropolitan residents who use an ED as a regular source of primary care to provide support for the main hypothesis. If the data do not support the hypothesis, the null hypothesis has support, and the central tendency will show much less variability than proposed in the main hypothesis. Reaves (1992) defined variability as the understanding of how similar or different categorical distributions are, but links this definition to variance and deviation, or the difference between a score and its average.

The central tendency in this analysis incorporated the mean, the median, and the mode of the statistical models formed via GDAHC, MDCH, and Modern Healthcare data sets. The variables in this analysis, items that may weaken the central tendency, are outlying health insurance holders with identifiable access to primary care. These variables did not affect the ability to make inferences about the effects of patient overcrowding on the health outcomes of patients. However, the mentioned variables did affect the operational definition of patient overcrowding examined in the first two chapters of this dissertation. Items that weakened central tendency in this study were measurements of objective standards for quality improvement and measuring health outcomes of patients without regular access to primary within the context of overcrowding.

Reliability and Validity

The data analysis proposed by this methodology placed a great deal of trust in the measurements defined above. The strength of conclusions presented later in this dissertation, and their link to the main hypothesis, have significant links to the repeatability of these measurements in future studies. Researchers who mostly use quantitative research methods define this strength as reliability. Reliability is the quality related to the probability that researchers can repeat measurements consistently in future studies (Reaves, 1992). However, many researchers who use quantitative methods admit that not all measurements are reliable and that modifications to those measurements in future studies might strengthen reliability. In other words, reliability of data in quantitative studies depends on the similarity of results when replicated (Reaves, 1992). In this study, random error within the quantitative data collection procedures from the GDAHC, MDCH, and Modern Healthcare databases directly affected the reliability of results.

While reliability is important, this study has the potential of proving that the main and null hypothesis are consistent and reliable across studies, yet the hypotheses could still misinform discussions of the results if they do not properly reflect the preliminary constructs (Reaves, 1992). Item analysis informs the construction of theoretical constructs and propositions present strong correlations with regular access to primary care, level of health insurance coverage where applicable, and patient overcrowding in a QI-informed framework. Item analysis is the examination of relationships between the probability that a claim is true and the overall measurements of central tendencies (Reaves, 1992). In the context of this study, if the central tendencies are broad and incorporate a large proportion of Detroit metropolitan residents who utilize the ED for primary care purposes, the data found lends itself to having increased validity.

Validity in Mixed Methods Research

Four types of validity are important when analyzing data from the use of mixed methods research. The first, *face validity*, has its basis on decisions of whether a construct is valid at face value. The second, *criterion validity*, is the result of the criterion comparisons linked to the construct measures themselves. Content validity encompasses all QI-based aspects of the original constructs while it also considers the relationship between measurements and any external variables (Reaves, 1992). Third, *content validity* refers to the extent of how measurements represent all of the different elements of a concept that is socially constructed. Different from face validity and criterion validity, content validity refers to having developed a working knowledge of the studied phenomenon (Reaves, 1992). Content validity, moreover, refers to evaluating whether assessments work for defining the concepts that emerge from the data. Finally, *construct validity* refers to the extent that assessments measure what they claim.

Alongside criterion and content validity, construct validity is a form of evidence that helps answer the research questions of a study (Reaves, 1992). Construct validity measures the appropriateness of inferences made based on observations or measurements made and specifically tests whether measures fit constructs (Reaves, 1992). Though this study is within the realm of health sciences, construct validity aids the data sampling and collection process by drawing from the social sciences, psychology, and language studies.

If the central tendency is broad after acknowledging face validity, the hypothesis of patient overcrowding as caused by a lack of regular access to primary care and a lack of health insurance are valid. If the results of data analysis show those measurements of quantitative data collection and the findings derived from qualitative data collection match, the original hypothesis will remain valid. If the content of the data analysis matches the general constructs in the theoretical propositions of healthcare-based QI approaches, as specifically linked to the main hypothesis, the methodology is valid.

Synthesis and Summary of Data

The objective of using mixed methods research is to lay out the specific aims of the research questions as well as the tools by which those aims are explored. The qualitative focus of this healthcare-based QI study is phenomenological, and the quantitative focus is on large- scale data collection. Together the data will be synthesized into a mixed methods approach that will inform a reliable, valid, and ethical investigation into the status of patient overcrowding in Detroit metropolitan area hospitals, and the related effects of primary care access and health insurance availability.

CHAPTER 4

Results–Presentation and Analysis of the Data

Overview

So far, the first three chapters cited the background and rationale for studying the problem of over-crowding in emergency departments (EDs) at hospitals in the Detroit Metropolitan Area. The background and rationale of this study indicated that the problem of patient overcrowding over the last 25 years was a significant research topic in the medical community (Chapter 1). As the amount of research, literature on this topic continues to grow, so do the causal links. Some of the earlier causes of ED over-crowding pointed to both input measures (non-urgent patients using the ED as a source of primary care), throughput measures (inadequate ED staffing), and output measures (shortages in the number of hospital beds). In nearly all cases, patient overcrowding reflects a much broader set of problems centered on issues of efficiency in the American health care system.

From November 1, 2014, to March 5, 2015, surveys were administered to ED staff at six locations of the Detroit Medical Center (DMC) in the metropolitan area of Detroit, Michigan.

The intent of using survey research in this study was to develop a quantitative measure of how patients access emergency medical services (EMS). Perceptions of attitudes from patients about the treatment they received from ED staff and other health professionals were also important to this study. The implications of this study extend to policy makers and academic researchers about the current state of ED wait times in Detroit and through the United States.

Most of the survey research took place between the hours of 7am to 11am and from between 7pm to 11pm Eastern Standard Time (EST). When patients entered the ED, research assistants explained the purpose of this study. Participants received informed consent from a brief oral script as research assistants assured that all answers would remain anonymous.

Choosing or not choosing to participate in the study had no negative consequences.

After entering triage, participants received a multiple-choice questionnaire about the length of time they waited to see a physician. Participants then received a sheet of paper that listed information on who to contact if any concerns were expressed. Data collection included information pertaining to the factors of age, gender, race/ethnicity, insurance status, chief complaint, triage acuity/severity level, and time spent in triage. Statistical analysis of survey results involved the use of stratified analysis and logistical regression.

This study also utilized a focus group comprised of key informants who had sufficient knowledge of emergency medicine, including operations and administrative processes, at most or all DMC hospital locations. ED staff members received a written invitation to participate in this study through their site managers. The invitation to participate requested that two representatives from nursing, two representatives from support services, one representative from medicine, one representative who practiced social work, and one representative from allied health professions at each DMC hospital participate in this study. All of the participants were part of the front-line staff at all DMC hospitals. At one DMC hospital, not all representatives were available to participate. In this case, in-depth interviews with one physician and two nurses were used for data collection.

Participants from focus groups at nearly all of the DMC hospitals received a print packet containing an information letter, an informed consent form, and a list of questions to discuss with their colleagues. Each focus group has a moderator chosen through a formal contracting procedure that emphasized prior experience and knowledge. Moderators prepared a guide for colleagues to follow for a free-flowing discussion ensuring that each point received adequate attention. Each focus group interview lasted approximately two hours. Moderators asked participants for clarification to provide background information about an issue raised during discussions. Each focus group was audio-recorded and transcribed for review and analysis.

Restatement of Research Problem

To restate what was mentioned in Chapter 1, the negative health outcomes that result from the problem of patient overcrowding have their backing in evidence-based research. Because of this problem, researchers developed a number of strategic models to identity the causes of patient overcrowding. Unfortunately, this problem remains in many urban hospitals for several reasons. While patients who wait in an ED have the option of accepting treatment in an outpatient primary care setting, most of these patients, prior to the signing of the Patient Protection and Affordable Care Act by President Barack Obama in 2010, do not have health insurance.

Research from the last ten years observed, despite interventions to solve problems associated with overcrowding, a continued rise in hospital admissions by patients accessing care through an ED (Bardsley et al., 2013). Innovation and cost are two issues that prevent hospital staff from institutionalizing systemic changes for reducing overcrowding and for improving the health outcomes of patients. Correlational research in this area of medical research links models of institutional change with several patient "controls" by collecting patient information by applying matching techniques to different patient scenarios (Bardsley et al., 2013). Studies in improvement science and quality management also provide insights into the development, implementation, refinement, and dissemination of innovative techniques used for reducing the negative effects of patient overcrowding (Bardsley et al., 2013).

Hospitals in the Detroit metropolitan area have a history of experiencing problems with lengthy wait times for ED patients. Recent economic issues pertaining specifically to the city of Detroit produced an environment in which low-income patients with little to no health insurance coverage utilized an ED a source of receiving primary care. Because of this problem, an assessment of primary care facilities in the Detroit metropolitan areas considered the variables of

patient overcrowding and lengthy wait times was necessary to understand the types of options that both hospital staff and patients have when delivering and receiving care.

Significant Trends and Themes in Data and Information

Results from surveys and focus groups pointed to themes associated with a "successful" ED and "service pressures" placed on ED staff. A successful ED clearly does not have the features associated with overcrowding due to a lack of available beds and available staff.

Services pressures referred to insights about barriers to serving patients efficiently and effectively while they also referred to anything that resulted in patient dissatisfaction.

Key Results of Implementing Research Design

Kotter's 8-Step Model is a useful model for implementing system-wide changes for decreasing ED wait times and improving health outcomes in patients. The PRECEDE/PROCEED Model also applies with reference to behaviors regarding predispositions among ED staff, reinforcing behaviors, and rewarding behaviors. Finally, applications of clinical microsystems using the HSE and Stufflebeam/CIPP change models identified the need for a greater degree of flexibility in making small changes at the local level.

Research Findings

The findings of this study attempted to answer two research questions by exploring the relationship between overcrowding and poor health outcomes for patients. Whereas the first research question wanted to know the current state of patient overcrowding in hospitals of the Detroit metropolitan area, the second research question sought to find a causal link between the problem of overcrowding and the health outcomes of patients who had to wait for more than six hours to receive care. By using a mixed methods correlational research model, this study used data from EDs located in Detroit metropolitan area hospitals. Qualitative methods involved a systematic analysis of textual descriptions accounting for the effects that patient overcrowding and lengthy wait times of more than six hours have on the health outcomes of low-income residents living in the Detroit metropolitan area. The study used quantitative measures to determine the strength of the relationship between patient overcrowding, wait times, and poor health outcomes.

Survey Results

Survey results indicated that, on a scale of 1 to 5, with "1" meaning "very poor" and "5" meaning "very good," participants at DMC hospitals had poor perceptions about the amount of time spent in triage before seeing a doctor. When receiving ambulatory surgery care, patients reported a "2" out of 5 when waiting to see a physician. Yet, perceptions about the waiting time before transferring to a treatment area led to an average rating among participants, as indicated by a mean score of "3." Participants also reported a mean score of "3" on survey results for three questions on length of waiting time before an ED staff member noticed a new arrival, comfort of the waiting area, and the likelihood of recommending the same ED at a DMC hospital to others.

The first three focus groups worked together on a sentence completion exercise to identify perceptions from participants about the outcomes, results, functions, and features of a "successful" ED. Participants were to complete a sentence starting with the phrase "A successful emergency department is not..." The sentence completion exercise also served to determine the types of outcomes that ED staff should avoid. Answers to sentence completion exercises for these focus groups were used to compare answers from discussions with the later three focus groups from three other DMC hospital locations.

A total of 37 participants worked on the sentence completion exercises, and responses to the sentence completion exercises varied. To start, 16 participants (43 percent) answered the sentence completion exercises by indicating that a successful ED is not "full or bogged down with admitted patients, medical patients, [and] intensive care unit (ICU) patients." Next, ten participants (27 percent) answered by indicating that a successful ED is not "a stressful, pressured or high-stress environment" while nine participants (24 percent) indicated that a successful ED is not "a holding unit for [an] alternate level of care (ALC) or a referral room for long-term care (LTC)." Seven participants (19 percent) answered the sentence completion exercise by noting that a successful ED is not "a 'dumping ground' for the health care system or a safety net for the hospital." The following four responses to the sentence completion exercises included answers from two participants each.

Two participants (5 percent) suggested that a successful ED is not "a personal clinic for consultants or for work-up of private patients while two others suggested that a successful ED is not "a unit for direct admissions or admissions from other facilities without beds." Moreover, two participants defined a successful ED as not "always functioning to the levels of overcapacity or 'gridlock'" while another two participants suggested that a successful ED is not "a free- standing emergency room." Aside from these responses to the sentence completion exercise, five participants (14 percent) indicated a response of "Other."

Focus Group Results

The total number of participants for each study group included eight emergency physicians, eight ED managers, and 42 ED staff (clinical nurses, allied health care professionals, social workers, and support staff). During each of the focus group interviews, application of the term "service pressures" provided some insights about the reasons for ED overcrowding at DMC hospitals. Some of the possible factors that focus group participants could choose ranged from patient characteristics, internal organizational problems, and problems considered outside the scope of an ED. Specific questions about how each focus group participant defined "services pressures," when service pressures were most likely to occur, and the strategies used for reducing service pressures were asked to gain an understanding of how to reduce ED waiting times and to improve health outcomes in patients.

Focus group participants provided two common definitions of "service pressures." While the first common definition referred to "anything that impedes the flow of patients through the ED, the second common definition referred to "[anything that] affects the quality of care delivered or results in patient frustration and/or stress to staff." The two definitions were the composite of several definitions among ED staff regarding "service pressures." Various definitions of "service pressures" amongst focus group participants included delays in patient assessment, diagnosis and treatment; overtaxing of resources; inadequate pace of service; inability to provide adequate care; and displays of dissatisfaction from patients and staff.

Research Question One

The first research question asked: What is the current state of patient overcrowding in Detroit area EDs? Answering this question involved taking a closer look inside the ED at Detroit Medical Center (DMC). Here, patient intake involves a triage process where hospital and nursing staff categorize patients based on the severity of their injury or medical condition.

Patients who use urgent care, walk-in services, or an emergency medical service (EMS) receive an assigned number from 1 (most serious) and 5 (the least serious) when reporting to the triage nurse. Patients assigned with a triage number of "1" or "2" require immediate attention from a physician while patients assigned with the number "3" should expect to see a physician within no more than 30 minutes.

Although a maximum wait time of 30 minutes is a guarantee according to DMC, some patients assigned with the number "3" reported having to wait for several hours in a waiting room. One possible reason for an increased wait time with patients assigned with the number "3" is simply because their injuries or medical conditions are not as serious and do not require immediate attention. Thus, the concerns of triage patients assigned with the number "3" do not have a high degree of priority. Although triage patients assigned the number "3" may wait up to several hours, patients assigned with the numbers "4" or "5" receive more quick and efficient service. Most patients assigned with a number "4" or "5" see a physician and receive a discharge shortly after their visit.

Triage systems similar to the one used at DMC use what Whitfield (2013) noted in her dissertation as using the Emergency Severity Index (ESI) that categorizes ED patients according to severity of injury or illness and patient resource needs. Yet ED overcrowding may have a link with difficulties in facilitating triage systems. Consistent triage systems lead to more accurate decision-making processes for assessing severity levels to patients (Whitfield, 2013). When hospitals use triage systems inconsistently, ED staff use subjective measures to assess the severity of injury or illness in patients. Inconsistent usage of triage systems among ED staff may also depend on the number of years acquired from professional experience. Continued training about changes in how hospitals use triage systems among ED staff is important for maintaining confidence in a system for delivering quality health care to patients in need (Whitfield, 2013).

Another reason for inconsistent usage of triage systems is the lack of documentation support when registered nurses (RNs) do not indicate the reasons for using and for not assigning numbers to patients using the ESI. Documentation support systems could help with improving not only the accuracy of patient information as they enter an ED, but they may also help with improving the health outcomes of patients with the most severe symptoms (Whitfield, 2013). Aside from making improvements in triage decision-making processes, documentation support systems lead to a more uniform triage process.

The Triage Process at Detroit Medical Center (DMC)

All patients at DMC have their information logged into a census that include data pertaining to the date of admission, hospital occupancy, number of available beds, and estimated waiting time. On average, DMC sees between 145 and 185 patients per day. The average number of time it takes for a patient to travel from entry until the point of admission depends on the number of patients waiting to see a physician. At DMC, the average distance that patients must travel from entry to admission is approximately 184 feet. Most patients who need to visit the ED at DMC arrive between the hours of 9 a.m. and 9 p.m. Walk-in patients typically go to a security guard or a liaison before receiving a triage assignment. In some cases, security guards or liaisons posed time constraints for receiving care from a triage nurse.

During the course of one month, patients arriving at the ED of DMC during daytime hours who were assigned to the triage unit had waited up to 3.8 hours. Patients assigned with the number "3" waited more than 30 minutes during peak daytime hours. The shortest wait time was ten minutes. Wait times during the evening and nighttime hours reached a maximum of two hours, though most patients who arrived during these times waited no more than 30 minutes.

The shortest waiting time during the evening and nighttime hours was 2.6 minutes. On more than half of the daytime shifts in a single month, patients waited two to three times as long in triage as they did during nighttime shifts.

Reasons for the increased wait times during the day include the heavy workload that triage nurses must complete. When overloaded with work, triage nurses are only able to treat 80 percent of their patients in a timely manner. Registration clerks at DMC also have issues with work overload while security guards and liaisons are not nearly as busy. Although triage nurses and registration clerks have high workloads, the cost of maintaining this staff amounts to approximately $450,000. Reducing the workload for triage nurses and registration clerks at DMC is important not only for lowering the costs of maintaining staff but also for improving the health outcomes of patients who may have to wait for a maximum of four hours in triage.

Wasting resources in terms of time and money poses significant barriers for patients to receive quality service and care. At DMC, issue related to overwork at the front end for triage nurses nd registration clerks led to a waste of time and money as much as it led to increased waiting times for patients during daytime hours.

While the issues in the ED at DMC presents only one example of problems related to patient over-crowding in Detroit area hospitals, reducing waste at the front end is critical. Lean Management principles may aid in reducing waste at the front end by identifying gaps and prioritizing activities. Some of the activities associated with Lean Management principles include re-balancing front-end processes by con-solidating the position of security guard with patient liaison. Security guards who act as patient liaisons should have the ability to assist patients and act as a gatekeeper to a more efficient process of receiving health care services. In addition, security guards who act as patient liaisons reduce the front-end workload of triage nurses and registration clerks by obtaining patient information at the point of entrance. Security guards then transfer patient information over to registration clerks for ensuring accuracy before further transferring patients to triage.

Reducing ED wait times by eliminating waste at the front end is a strategy involving evidence-based research on nursing shift handovers as reflecting communication patterns in clinical practice (Athanasakis, 2013). While shift handovers have their use for improving efficiency of service and care for patients be-tween daytime and nighttime hours, effective communication practices are critical for ensuring that pa-tients do not have excessive wait times. Handovers are important when security guards must act as patient liaisons as accurate information about the extent of an injury or an illness determines the level of attention received (Athanasakis, 2013). Miscommunication may cause greater harm in patients. If hospital staff at the front end of an ED do not receive proper training on how to communicate patient information, patients are less likely to receive quality and timely care (Athanasakis, 2013). If patients require immediate attention and possibly an overnight stay, the accurate transferring of information about any collected specimens from patients is important for maintaining quality care. Depending on the number assigned to patients in triage, the types of patient information transferred between front end staff varies. Accurately categorizing patients according to triage assignment is essential for managing patient flow between shifts who must handle multiple cases in their practice on an everyday basis.

Reducing waste at the front end of an ED also depends on recognizing the commonalities of medical needs in patients (Donahue, Cunnion, Balaban, & Sochats, 2012). Depending on the type of hospital and its location, an ED can plan strategically for varying patient scenarios to serve medical care more effectively. Especially for hospitals in the Detroit metropolitan area, the need to serve populations most affected by health crises and even violent crimes should not come without addressing the specific needs of each patient (Donahue et al., 2012). Objective measures used across different patient scenarios leads to hospital staff developing a greater sense of preparedness in terms of delivering both efficient and effective medical attention.

Research by Donahue and colleagues (2012) referred to the use of an All Hazards approach that calls for hospital to institute plans and actions across a wide variety of patient scenarios for reducing hazards and risk. Effective response to different patient scenarios affects the health outcomes and resiliency of patients who must seek emergency medical services.

Another way of describing this approach is by referring to the concept of "citizen preparedness" in assuming that knowing the best course of action should consider the immediate needs of patients in mind when delivering medical care. An all hazards approach, along with an application of Lean Management principles, may not only promote greater efficiency and effectiveness in the delivery of medical care, it may promote improvements in psychological and social welfare (Donahue et al., 2012). Here, improving perceived levels of confidence in an entire health care system by patients is critical because of the social and political implications.

Educational interventions are important for reducing the problem of ED overcrowding in Detroit metropolitan area hospitals because they reduce negative health outcomes in patients who demonstrate at-risk behaviors (Houry et al., 2011). Public health issues in low-income areas, including issues of intimate partner violence (IPV) and substance abuse are worth noting because of how ED staff handles patient information.

The research by Houry and colleagues (2011) explains that low-income populations, including populations that have a racial and ethnic minority status, demonstrate greater susceptibility for cardiovascular disease caused by smoking and alcohol consumption. While individual risk factors are different, the effects are cumulative. Smoking and alcohol consumption in low-income populations has a presumable link to increased levels of IPV while, at the same time, these at-risk behaviors lead to the development of depressive disorders in children and adults (Houry et al., 2011). Educational interventions for low-income populations that display the cumulative effects of at-risk behaviors should may help improve health outcomes for these patients who must visit an ED for the reasons already stated.

Perceptions of ED Overcrowding Among ED Staff at DMC Locations

Study participants believed that ED overcrowding is a frequently occurring problem at all DMC locations. ED overcrowding can occur multiple times within a single day, with some hours indicating significantly higher amounts of activity. Aside from specific times of day, some seasons periods of ED overcrowding are easy to predict, especially during winter. Participants also indicated that media reports of contagious diseases led to an inability to predict overcrowding. ED overcrowding turns patient flow into an inefficient process. As a result, study participants identified several causes. ED managers and front-line staff at DMC hospitals identified a shortage of available beds and lack of available nursing staff as the two most significant causes of overcrowding. Preliminary results generated from sentence completion exercises provided strong support for participants who identified the perceived causes of ED overcrowding. From the sentence completion exercises, a dominant theme that emerged was a recognition among ED staff about the changing roles at each member must play while at work.

Shortage of available beds.

Focus group participants held the perception that the lack of available beds and stretchers for ED patients was a direct cause of overcrowding. The number of admitted patients held in triage was often more than the number of available beds at nearly all DMC locations during peak times and seasons. Participants actually perceived that admitted patients posed significant barriers among ED staff to access available beds and stretchers. This result suggests that periods of ED overcrowding lead to greater work burdens among focus group participants. However, this result also suggests that focus group participants perceived the cause of ED overcrowding as linked with a shortage of floor nurses, high numbers of in-patients waiting for a transfer to another care unit, and more severe injuries and symptoms of illnesses among regular patients as well as among ED patients.

Lack of available nursing staff.

Focus group participants perceived that nursing shortages contributed to ED overcrowding at all DMC hospital locations. Front-end nurses reported that they were frequently asked to work more hours while nearly all focus group participants reported that the limited availability of non-nursing staff placed greater burdens on nurses. Nurses perceived greater work burdens during peak hours and seasons, as well as during weekends and evening shifts. Along with regular duties, nurses reported that they greeted patients, drew blood, cleaned rooms, and arranged transport. Caring for both new and already admitted patients posed significant challenges for nurses. Nurses also reported having to fulfill the requests of physicians to care for disparate groups of patients. Under ED conditions, nurses reported feeling uncomfortable in having to care for new patients while also having to care for already admitted patients.

The changing role of E.Ds.

Focus group participants perceived that a shortage of available beds and stretchers led to changing expectations about the role that an ED plays at all DMC hospital locations. Participants believed that non-emergency staff should treat an ED as a functioning unit belonging to an entire health care system. Other expectations among participants included perceptions that non-emergency staff administer tests and complete paperwork before admitting patients or before transferring patients to a different care unit.

Participants argued transferring patients increased LOS in patients as they waited for results from laboratory tests.

Suggestions for Interventions to Alleviate ED Overcrowding

Study participants suggested efforts for improving throughput measures to address capacity issues at DMC hospitals and within a health care system. Proposed throughput measures included: quicker turnaround times for laboratory and diagnostic imaging services; a sufficient number of staff other than nurses available to greet patients, including laboratory technicians and support staff; providing opportunities for patients to access community and palliative care services (Bardsley, Stevenson, Smith, & Dixon, 2013); and faster responses from specialists. Proposed interventions for improving capacity issues within a health care system included. Establishing a holding unit for admitted patients, an observation unit managed by ED staff and located near a DMC hospital, providing round-the-clock outpatient service, introducing an internal transportation services for patients between sites, and increasing the number of available beds for severe and long-term patients based on patient need and situational demands placed on ED staff. System-wide improvements, according to the study participants, would also emphasize the importance of adequate funding and medical resources.

Research Question Two

This research question asked: How does ED overcrowding affect the health outcomes of patients who must wait in excess of six hours to receive care? One study noted that, along with ED overcrowding, ambulance diversion to hospitals in different locations presented a significant problem for achieving positive health outcomes in patients (Mendosa, 2009). Both ED overcrowding and ambulance diversion comprise the quality of care that hospitals may provide, though ambulance diversion tends to cause greater frustration among registration clerks and triage nurses at the front end. Nurse-to-patient ratios are typically higher in an ED (Mendosa, 2009). Because of this, health outcomes are contingent upon the number of available beds and the number of available physicians who can efficiently, and effectively address the needs of each patient. Operational models in an ED, whether they are triage or fast track, also determine the health outcomes of patients (Marmor, Golany, Israelit, & Mandelbaum, 2012). Hospitals of varying sizes and in different locations use operational models unique for the types of scenarios they are likely to encounter. Social and demographic factors set the parameters for the types of patients that hospitals serve. For example, hospitals that serve an aging population may operate more efficiently and effectively by using a fast-track model than they would using a triage model (Marmor et al., 2012). Conversely, hospitals that serve mostly at-risk populations may have more optimal outcomes when using a triage model.

One consistent problem found in many hospitals located in the Detroit metropolitan area refers to the length of stay (LOS) as a rarely noted aspect when ED staff admit and treat patients (Marmor et al., 2012). While a triage model may reduce the average LOS, non-urgent patients who use an ED benefit from using a fast-track model. Alternatively, while fast-track models serve non-urgent patients, many of which use an ED as a source of primary care, they have more demonstrable effects on patients with more severe injuries or illnesses (Marmor et al., 2012). In one example, Hickman and Ojo (2013) noted how patients with chronic obstructive pulmonary disease (COPD) account for almost 20 percent of daily ED admissions. Most admissions of patients with COPD require stays averaging 6.5 days (Hickman & Ojo, 2013). ED admissions for patients with COPD pose significant barriers for the efficient and effective delivery of medical care because of a lack in available beds.

The study by Hickman and Ojo (2013) used a change model over the course of five months that supported early discharge for patients with severe COPD who using hospitals with a fast track system. A change model for this patient scenario extended the All Needs approach used by Donahue and colleagues (2012) by collaboration with primary and secondary care facilities to determine the suitability of patients to receive an early discharge (Hickman & Ojo, 2013). During their study, Hickman and Ojo (2013) found that only one patient with severe COPD symptoms required re-admission within 30 days. The results of this study suggested that implementing a change model has significant implications for improving the health outcomes of patients who require admission into an ED. However, implementing a change model should involve gradual steps that encourage reflection and professional development measures in hospital staff at all levels (Hickman & Ojo, 2013). Change models that emphasize the use of fast-track models for discharging patients with either severe or non-urgent injuries and illnesses lead to a more positive experience because of how different care facilities collaborate and maintain accurate patient records that easily transfer between ED staff.

Kotter's 8-Step Model

The change model used in the study by Hickman and Ojo (2013) applied Kotter's 8-Step Model. This model assists health professionals in managing multiple time lines, create a better organizational vision, and build coalitions with other health professionals (Hickman & Ojo, 2013). Kotter's 8-Step Model applies the following steps during a triage process:

1. Establish a sense of urgency;
2. Form a strong guiding coalition;
3. Create a sense of vision;
4. Communicate the vision;
5. Empower others to act on a sense of vision;
6. Plan and create short-term success;
7. Consolidate improvements and continue to produce change; and
8. Institutionalize new approaches (Hickman & Ojo, 2013).

Establish a sense of urgency. Hickman and Ojo (2013) observed that the first step of Kotter's 8-Step Model—establishing a sense of urgency—involved developing a service model for training ED staff to recognize the possible outcomes for COPD patients. ED staff received training on the coordination and management of worsened conditions after admission by facilitating an early discharge to reduce the length of stay. ED staff also received training on pulmonary rehabilitation, integrated oxygen service, and end of life referral and support (Hickman & Ojo, 2013). Encouraging patients to manage COPD symptoms effectively leads to a reduce length of stay. In turn, COPD patients who manage their symptoms have a decreased likelihood of readmission.

Establishing a sense of urgency in this context therefore involves creating an organizational culture that emphasizes group affiliation and coordination. The organizational culture involves training ED staff in *acute medicine* (Hickman & Ojo, 2013). Here, ED staff receives appropriate training that prevents them from delaying the triage process when assessing the future health outcomes of patients. Successful training in acute medicine involves strong and consistent leadership so that patients receive accurate placement according to the severity of their COPD symptoms (Hickman & Ojo, 2013). Accurate placement of patients, however, should involve timely dedication to recognizing COPD symptoms through collaborate efforts with health professionals who have specialized training in cardiovascular disease.

In another example, healthcare utilization data from EDs throughout the United States analyzed changes in influenza-like illness during a recent outbreak (Kass-Hout et al., 2012). The study used a change point analysis to detect changes in the number of patients admitted into an ED with influenza-like symptoms. Kass-Hout and colleagues (2012) combined their change point analysis with an Early Aberration Reporting System (EARS) algorithm to detect change points in daily time-series data using a network from the Distribute project. The influenza outbreak studied occurred during the 2008-9 and 2009-10 seasons. For the 2008-9 flu seasons, Kass-Hout and colleagues (2012) detected 21 change points. Influenza-like activity in patients admitted into an ED indicated an increased trend across 12 change points and decreased trends anine change points. For the 2009-10 flu seasons, Kass-Hout and colleagues (2012) detected 11 change points, with influenza-like activity increasingly significantly after two change points and decreasing nine times. The results of this research suggests that data collection that analyzes multiple trends may promote a greater sense of urgency among ED staff for recognizing the range of influenza-like symptoms in admitted patients.

Form a strong guiding coalition. Accurately recognizing the severity of COPD symptoms, along with the severity of other illnesses or injuries, should take place in a professional setting with a positive climate. ED staff should work as part of a team open to change (Hickman & Ojo, 2013). The study by Hickman and Ojo (2013) observed the effects of working collaboratively between primary and secondary care based on the common caseload of patients. Building a coalition for improving the health outcomes of patients with COPD symptoms entailed an assemblage of health professionals with fitting talents and skills to advance an organizational mission. When working collaboratively, ED staff in primary and secondary care units holds regular meetings for brainstorming ideas of how to improve the quality of delivering care (Hickman & Ojo, 2013). Regular meetings provide ED staff with opportunities for sharing knowledge and information about a variety of patient situations.

The purpose of holding regular meetings is to define organizational objectives and articulate goals clearly, so that all ED staff understands and have updated information about how to handle specific patient cases (Hickman & Ojo, 2013). Regular meetings also provide opportunities for ED staff to recognize differences in professional training that may pose barriers to delivering efficient and effective delivery of health care. When meetings take place, a strong sense of leadership is an important feature for ensuring the best possible health outcomes (Hickman & Ojo, 2013). A strong sense of leadership ensures that someone with more expertise on how triage processes work can better direct less professionally trained ED staff into promoting positive health outcomes while also promoting shortened wait times and a shortened length of stay.

Create a sense of vision. Meeting optimal goals for decreasing wait times, decreasing LOS, and improving the health outcomes of patients should have benchmarked goals indicating a target number of patients that it would like to see admitted and discharged on a weekly basis.

Changes to the triage process of admitting patients and using an ESI to assign patients according to the severity of their injury or illness should come with a clear and consistent vision communicated to ED staff at all levels (Hickman & Ojo, 2013). While predicting the number of admitted and discharged patients on a weekly basis is not always possible, predicting whether symptoms will worsen or improve is almost as impossible. Encouraging lower waiting times in ED patients while also encouraging a shortened LOS should involve ED staff facilitating follow- up interventions for monitoring the progress of conditions in admitted patients (Hickman & Ojo, 2013). Creating a vision for meeting optimal goals in health care delivery systems should ideally include the combined efforts of nurses and physicians with extensive training in acute medicine. The input of pharmacists is also important. Importantly, communicating information between ED staff about the health status of patients should not use lengthy explanations of how to manage and treat conditions (Hickman & Ojo, 2013). In all cases, ED staff at all levels should understand how the value of implementing organizational changes affects the overall vision.

Communicate the vision. Because the triage process can seem incredibly complex, communicating thoughts, ideas, and information through verbal and non-verbal channels helps provide descriptors of the internal and external problems occurring with the health care profession (Hickman & Ojo, 2013). Problems of communication occur at all levels; however, they should not pose any risk of negatively affecting the health outcomes of patients with the most severe injuries or illnesses. Personal assessments of communication issues may lead to conflicts over how to effectively treat patients and ensure the best health outcomes possible.

Training at various levels of ED staff may also lead to conflict because of gaps in knowledge regarding how to handle patients with conditions requiring the attention of a qualified specialist (Hickman & Ojo, 2013). Regular meetings among ED staff about how to improve the quality of a health care delivery system should discuss how to recognize the tone of verbal and non-verbal communication so that conflict do not occur. Regular meetings are also important for ensuring that ED staff maintain an organizational vision or revise it where necessary (Hickman & Ojo, 2013). As is the case with forming a strong coalition, a strong sense of leadership among experience health professionals should encourage perceptions of positive organizational change for ED staff at all levels. Leadership can also take place at all levels when each ED staff member pursues different lines of communication to achieve similar outcomes for patients.

Empower others to act on a sense of vision. Leadership in an ED organization should provide necessary steps for empowering health professionals and allowing them to make informed yet effective decisions about how to ensure positive health outcomes in patients (Hickman & Ojo, 2013). Recognizing the individual motivations of each ED staff member for working in the health care industry should involve collaborative efforts determining whether a triage unit is the best place for some health professionals to work. Some newly trained ED staff may find perceive that working in an ED is fascinating; however, ED staff must have the capacity to handle large amounts of patient information in a short amount of time while they must also have the capacity to assess patients accurately.

Accurate patient assessments upon entering an ED waiting room by ED staff requires having a strong sense of human agency to acquire the training necessary for making sense of information (Hickman & Ojo, 2013). In the context of communicating to improve the organizational mission of a hospital like DMC, providing opportunities to communicate important knowledge about the conditions of patients assigned a low ESI number should come with a high degree of trust. However, if some newly trained ED staff does not perceive themselves as having a high degree of self-efficacy, then they should feel empowered to request an assignment to a different area of the hospital until after completing a certificate-training program (Hickman & Ojo, 2013). While newly trained ED staff can enroll in formal courses to improve their knowledge about the adverse health conditions they are likely to observe in patients entering an ED, leadership has the responsibility of delivering a consistent message. At the same time, resistance to adapt new knowledge among established ED staff may also require formal training modules that help reduce problems of communication (Hickman & Ojo, 2013). Formal training modules for ED staff with varying degrees of professional experience can therefore help reduce ED wait times, reduce LOS, and improve overall health outcomes in patients.

Plan and create short-term successes. This step of Kotter's model encourages ED staff to celebrate short-term positive results; however, ED staff should not celebrate successful steps

in reducing ED wait times or of improving health outcomes in patients too early (Hickman & Ojo, 2013). Efforts made to decrease ED wait time and improve health outcomes in patients deserve praise, though they should not lead ED staff into a state of complacency. Setting goals is appropriate for members of ED staff at all levels, especially in reference to factors like patient demographics, severity of injury or illness, and LOS.

In the study by Hickman and Ojo (2013), the COPD team set a goal of facilitating the early release of two patients per week because one out of four patients with COPD were not eligible for early release. Knowing what patients need should encourage ED staff to facilitate early release while it should also encourage reduced ED wait times. Patients with a variety of injuries or illness who have an assigned ESI number of "4" or "5" are most likely eligible for early release while patients assigned with an ESI number of "3" greater may need to have more extended stays.

Consolidate improvements and continue to produce change. Recommendations for alleviating the problem of ED overcrowding at DMC hospitals should follow what Hickman and Ojo (2013) cited as "assisted-discharge schemes" offered to select patients (p. 156). Short- and long-term aims are both important when consolidating improvement efforts, and ED staff must strike an appropriate balance between reaching these aims. According to Kotter's Model, short- term successes typically last six months with assisted-discharge schemes indicating an early release of one to two patients per week (Hickman & Ojo, 2013). Short-term results often keep urgency levels high among ED staff. Thus, regular training interventions help with exposing inexperience ED staff to the tools needed for meeting organizational objectives. Feedback from training interventions should pertain to specific clinical settings and emergencies for the right changes to occur. However, the training interventions should provide enough flexibility for ED staff to accommodate patients in a range of care settings.

For example, training interventions may recognize differences in treatment according to gender. In their study on patients waiting to receive a brain-imaging scan, Madsen and colleagues (2015) found that women wait longer and are less likely to receive an intravenous tissue plasminogen activator (tPA). Findings from the study conducted by Madsen and colleagues (2015) point to the importance of the ED triage process when properly assessing patients with signs of stroke. Although no survey and focus group results pointed to gender- based differences in treatment, the triage process may effectively contribute to these disparities. Proper assessment of stroke patients, along with proper ESI assignments, determines the number of available beds for women who arrive at an ED within six hours of symptom onset (Madsen et al., 2015). For stroke patients of all genders, health outcomes depend on performing brain scans within 25 minutes of arrival, administering an IV tPA within 60 minutes of arrival, keeping the patient alive between admission and discharge, and ensuring that stroke patients receive a thorough yet efficient discharge (Madsen et al., 2015). An important point to draw from the study by Madsen and colleagues (2015) is that while no significant differences exist in treating male and female patients, more observable differences may seem apparent in differences of treatment according to race and ethnicity.

Institutionalize new practices. According to Kotter's 8-Step Model, this step is the ultimate goal for providing solutions to the problem of ED overcrowding and for improving health outcomes in patients. Solving these problems is not an easy process. At the same time, improving perceptions of experiences in an ED among patients and their families involves multiple factors (Hickman & Ojo, 2013). Strategies that encourage the early release of patients with less urgent injuries or illnesses pertain to decreasing LOS, increasing patient satisfaction, working collaboratively between primary and secondary care unites, and broadening the scope of medical knowledge among ED staff (Hickman & Ojo, 2013). Gauging the success of strategies used to reduced ED overcrowding and improve health outcomes should involve an ongoing analysis about the effects of releasing patients early. This can involve follow-up procedures to ensure that DMC hospitals properly institutionalize strategies needed for making improvements.

Because of the need to acknowledge short-term successes, ED staff should recognize that the institutionalization of new practices is actually a long-term process (Hickman & Ojo, 2013). Full and proper institutionalization of new practices must involve ED staff generating a significant degree of trust that solving the problem of ED overcrowding at DMC hospitals will eventually lead to long-term success. Yet, while trust is important, ED managers will likely benefit from developing measures for conducting strong internal audits to ensure that newly institutionalized practices emphasize long-term sustainability. Measuring internal audits, however, depends on recognizing a need for changing the professional behaviors of ED staff.

The next section describes a possible model that ED staff at DMC hospitals may use to develop more efficient means of delivering care to patients, and improving health outcomes while attempting to solve the problem of overcrowding by using a triage model to reduce wait times.

PRECEDE/PROCEED Planning Model

Leonard and colleagues (2012) selected the PRECEDE/PROCEED model of behavioral change based on how it provides an "in-depth understanding of why a behavior occurs" and "provides guidance for behavior changes based on the determinants of the behavior" (pp. 163-4). The PRECEDE/PROCEED model recognizes the barriers and motivators for positive and negative professional behaviors. Barriers and motivators include predispositions among ED staff in terms of personal knowledge, attitudes, and beliefs; reinforcement of organizational and cultural norms with reference to social support systems and workplace norms; and enabling factors of organizational expertise, structures, resources, and processes that determine behavior (Leonard et al., 2012). Data using this model resulted in an expansion of the research process by providing correlations to determinants of behavior and by implying suggestions for designing strategies for improving training models among ED staff.

Barriers to change. In using their PRECEDE/PROCEED model, Leonard and colleagues (2012) identified 17 different factors that reduced the likelihood of ED staff addressing ED overcrowding and patient health outcomes effectively. In terms of factors related to predispositions among ED staff, concern for patient safety, lack of clarity in research purposes, fear of liability, perceived lack of confidence, negative perceptions among healthcare providers, and lack of professionalization posed significant barriers. Negative reinforcing factors that discouraged ED staff from making changes to healthcare delivery processes included inadequate preparation and lack of feedback and rewards for participating in quality improvement programs (Leonard et al., 2012). Finally, negative enabling factors that hinder effective health care delivery to ED patients included. A lack of situational awareness about the severity of injury or illness in patients; overwork; time constraints; lack of knowledge on how to conduct research; conflicts with existing professional standards on how to implement change models; organizational resistance to change; and incomplete organizational infrastructures (Leonard et al., 2012). Despite recognizing these barriers to change, Leonard and colleagues (2012) noted that very few research efforts to date provide identifiable links between changes needed at the provider and agency levels. Barriers to change have cognitive and social elements while they may also have their basis in required organizational processes.

Motivators of change. The PRECEDE/PROCEED model identified 12 motivational factors likely to increase the likelihood that ED staff will address the problems associated with ED overcrowding and subsequent health outcomes in effective ways. *Positive* factors related to predispositions among ED staff included the recognition of identifiable benefits to patient care and improvements made in professional practice (Leonard et al., 2012). Positive reinforcing factors included the use of feedback from ED nurses, and physicians about patient care includes taking pride in working for a healthcare organization; promoting an organizational culture that values the importance of research needed for improving quality of healthcare delivery systems; approval for administering special medical procedures from administration, and medical doctors. Additionally, understanding that participating in quality management programs enhances the scope of research; participation in previous studies that advanced the healthcare profession; and compensation for work performed (Leonard et al., 2012). Finally, positive enabling factors included the provision of adequate training and resources. The general suggestion from Leonard and colleagues (2012) is that enabling factors have important links with policy outcomes that influence behavior and affect health outcomes in patients. Yet, because changes at the local hospital level do not always lead to systemic changes, the use of system management tools for improving healthcare delivery systems are worth noting as described in the next section.

Clinical Microsystems and the HSE Change Model

In her dissertation, O'Dwyer (2014) used the HSE Change Model based on an organizational approach for developing a framework to implement change into practice. O'Dwyer (2014) also used the Stufflebeam evaluation model to, first, assess the success resulting from hospitals implementing microsystems into practice and, second, evaluate improvements in the health outcomes of patients. Microsystems depend on the establishment of quality improvement measures by ED staff members who undergo training for implementing small-scale changes into an ED (O'Dwyer, 2014). The main purpose of implementing small-scale changes is to promote independence among ED staff without the need for too much intervention from management. A secondary purpose of microsystems is to involve patients in the inputs and outputs of healthcare delivery systems (O'Dwyer, 2014). Microsystems allow ED staff to communicate with patients about possible types of service they may receive.

HSE Change Model. This framework for organizational change to an ED identifies the need for leaders to maintain a degree of flexibility and to develop the capacity for recognizing where small changes to healthcare delivery processes are necessary (O'Dwyer, 2014). Core principles of using an HSE Change Model refer to improving the quality of care for patients, staff engagement, involvement in change, and providing consistent approaches to patient scenarios with similar characteristics (O'Dwyer, 2014). The core principles of an HSE Change ensure successful implementation of microsystems at each step of the process. When stakeholders initiate the implementation of microsystems, they ensure that changes have positive effects from start to finish and those changes to healthcare delivery systems depend on context (O'Dwyer, 2014). Ensuring positive changes to healthcare delivery systems suggest changes to the organizational culture of an ED for continued monitoring of quality improvement programs.

The Stufflebeam/CIPP Model. Also known as, the CIPP (Context, Input, Process, Product) model, the Stufflebeam Model evaluates the effectiveness of processes used for changing the organizational culture of an industry (O'Dwyer, 2014). Whereas *context* is one evaluative element important for assessing goals and priorities of a microsystem by performing a needs assessment, *input* is another element that evaluates alternative processes allowing for comparisons between microsystems to ensure standards of quality (O'Dwyer, 2014). *Process* is the third element of the Stufflebeam Model that assesses the implementation of a quality improvement project while *product* is the evaluation stage that assesses the impact, effectiveness, and outcomes of implemented changes to organizational culture.

Using this model for improving quality management systems has plenty of documentation because of how many industries use both formative and summative evaluations of change programs (O'Dwyer, 2014). Overall, applications of Stufflebeam/CIPP Model suggests that healthcare professionals have an imperative to improve quality management systems at the local level for improving patient outcomes in terms of decreased waiting times in an ED and positive health prognoses upon approval for discharge. At the same time, while implementing local changes at a specific hospital location, structural changes made to diffusion processes have important implications for the feedback that ED staff receive when implementing quality improvement programs (Neuwirth, Peck, & Simonović, 2015). Not only do structural changes apply for improving the delivery of healthcare services, they also apply to nearly all other industries.

Synthesis and Summary of Data The findings of this study attempted to explore the relationship between ED overcrowding and poor health outcomes. Survey results for the first research question of how ED staff at DMC hospitals can reduce patient wait times indicated that study participants had negative perceptions about observing increased wait times. Answers from survey results indicated a variety of factors that contributed to a "successful" ED. While 16 participants believed that a successful ED did not have features of overcrowding, ten participants believed that a successful ED did not exhibit signs of significant pressures placed on staff. Some of the survey results suggested that a successful ED was not a holding unit for ALC or long-term patients while other results suggested that an ED is not a "dumping ground" or a "safety net" for patients without primary means of obtaining care. Moreover, some of the survey results suggested that a successful ED should avoid overcrowding.

Focus group results for the first research question attempted to define the meaning of "service pressures" by probing for insights from ED staff about the reasons for overcrowding at DMC hospitals. Two common definitions of "service pressures" were identified from interviews with focus group participants. The first definition referred to anything that prevent an efficient patient flow while the second definition referred to anything in the delivery of healthcare that results in patient dissatisfaction. Other types of services pressures defined by focus group participants included delays in assessing, diagnosing, and treating patients; overuse of resources; inadequate service pace, and an inability to provide adequate care.

Perceptions of ED overcrowding at DMC hospitals indicated that some times of day and seasons of the year were more likely to produce this problem. The two main causes of ED overcrowding at DMC hospitals, according to participating ED staff, were a shortage of available beds and a lack of available nursing staff. Focus group participants perceived that these two reported causes of ED overcrowding led to changing expectations about the role that an ED plays in improving health outcomes. Some changes to expectations include perceptions that non- emergency staff administers tests and complete paperwork before admitting or transferring patients to a different care unit. Suggestions for interventions to solve the problem of ED overcrowding included proposed changes to throughput measures including: quicker turn-around times for lab and diagnostic services, sufficient staffing to greet patients, opportunities for patients to access community-based and palliative care, and faster responses from specialists.

Other proposed interventions included: establishing a holding unit for admitted patients; an observation unit managed by ED staff and located near a DMC hospital; providing round-the- clock outpatient services; introducing an internal transportation service for patients between sites; and increasing the number of available beds for acute and long-term patients based on patient need and situational demands placed on ED staff.

Answering the second research question involved applying studies that used different change models for improving the quality of healthcare delivery systems. One consistent problem found at DMC hospitals was an increased length of stay (LOS) in patients with more severe injuries or illness. Triage models may benefit these patients while patients who present less urgent cases might fare better from a fast-track model. The first model applied was Kotter's 8-Step Model that assists health professionals with managing multiple patient cases, create a clearer organizational vision, and build coalitions with other health professionals. The steps of establishing a sense of urgency, forming a strong guiding coalition, creating a sense of vision, communicating the vision, empowering others to act on the sense of vision, planning and creating short-term successes, consolidating improvement and continuing to produce change, and institutionalizing new practices are all important in this change model. However, the second change model—PRECEDE/PROCEED—applies behavioral changes to an organizational culture by recognizing barriers and motivators of change.

The PRECEDE/PROCEED model identified positive and negative factors related to predispositions among ED staff, reinforcing behaviors, and rewarding behaviors. The final change model used in this study applied to clinical microsystems using the HSE and Stufflebeam/CIPP models. While the HSE Change Model identifies the need for ED managers to maintain a degree of flexibility for developing the capacity for recognizing where small changes make a large difference, the Stufflebeam/CIPP Model evaluates the effectiveness of processes useful for changing an organizational culture by analyzing the elements of contexts, input, process, and product. The implication is that structural changes for solving the problem of ED overcrowding and improving health outcomes in patients receive formative and summative evaluations of programs implemented to improve the quality of healthcare delivery.

Contribution to Applied Practices Developing a strong change model for solving the problems of ED overcrowding and improving health outcomes in patients has conceptual and theoretical links to a Transtheoretical Model (TTM) as understood by Wells and colleagues (2013). A TTM investigates levels of awareness in patients about the severity of their injury or illness, while it also investigates considerations for patients deciding participate and remain in treatment for their conditions (Wells et al., 2013). Future research in quality management may benefit from exploring the barriers and facilitators for providing care to patients with a variety of ailments. ED staff at all levels should have adequate training about the emergencies they are most likely to see.

Perceptions among patients about their own medical conditions should inform ED staff about the interventions they may need to use for ensuring that they receive efficient and adequate care.

Especially for patients who must visit an ED because of psychiatric issues related to depression (Wells et al., 2013), ED staff at all levels should have relatively similar amounts of information readily available to aid in the process of administering care.

In the event of emergency situations that involve disasters and sudden outbreaks of disease, training among ED staff on how to use social media platforms can help leverage data to provide insights during these times (Cassa et al., 2013). Messages posted to Twitter and Facebook during the Boston Marathon set an example for how ED staff can respond more efficiently to severe emergencies within minutes of their occurrence. Data analysis from messages posted on Facebook and Twitter has implications for public safety officers who must know the specific locations of where disasters occur (Cassa et al., 2013). However, while social media has its uses, one potential drawback to note is that messages posted on Facebook and Twitter may present false positive reports with negative consequences on the health outcomes of patients with severe injuries from disasters or severe illnesses caused by sudden outbreaks of disease. Cassa and colleagues (2013) therefore suggest that classification strategies and filtering approaches used specifically for disease surveillance and crime tracking may refine sensitivity towards scrutinizing messages for accurate information about disasters and outbreaks.

Data collection in future studies that focus on solving the problem of ED overcrowding at DMC hospital locations may generate greater amounts of information originating in social media platforms (Cassa et al., 2013). Classification strategies and filtering approaches assist public safety officers and ED staff in locating instances of major disasters and sudden disease outbreaks. However, another potential drawback to ED staff using social media for collecting data from patient information is the perceived costs of these interventions. Related to this drawback is the cost of not reacting appropriately to emergencies that initially gain publicity on Facebook and Twitter (Cassa et al, 2013). Natural disasters and outbreaks of disease that last longer than expected require more in-depth investigation, especially when reducing the potential for false positives to emerge from data collection.

Theoretical implications of quality management are worth noting. Theory can strengthen quality improvement programs by facilitating their effectiveness despite the reputation of theory as overly confusing (Davidoff, Dixon-Woods, Leviton, & Michie, 2015). Theory is both formal and informal because of its importance to nearly every human act. Davidoff and colleagues (2015) proposed that future research should evaluate grand, mid-range, and program theories of quality management. A primary reason for considering theoretical implications of quality management is the tendency for researchers to either misuse or not use theory at all. Research in grand, mid-range, and program theories of quality management provides tools for examining the criteria for what makes a "good" theory and for emphasizing the values and challenges of combining theory based in personal experience with formally developed theory (Davidoff et al., 2015). While theory based in personal experience may inform future research in quality improvement programs, health professionals are not always aware of how to develop strong practical applications. Thus, more effective formal theories of practice that combine personal and professional experiences will help clarify assumptions that are often biased, distorted, and limited in scope (Davidoff et al., 2015). Applying formal theories of quality management as understood from personal experiences of working in the health professions should aid ED staff into maximizing all of the possible learning opportunities and promote the transfer of knowledge between different hospitals units.

The future of healthcare delivery systems depends on strategies that reshape how patients think about the ways that doctors and nurses provide care. Innovations made to the healthcare delivery system at DMC hospitals should maximize health outcomes. At the same time, innovations should also foster patient value and affordability (Tabish & Syed, 2015). Patients expect high levels of quality when receiving health care. As a result, the healthcare industry has indicated a growing trend in moving towards "data-driven" methods for closely monitoring unusual situations (Tabish & Syed, 2015). However, while data-driven methods lead to both more efficient and more accurate systems of information, the pace of adapting these methods is very slow. It is imperative to establish the right training programs for ED staff, to learn about data-driven methods.

Leaders in the healthcare industry prioritize infrastructure and governance practices that support value-based models while healthcare providers profit from fee-for-service revenues (Tabish & Syed, 2015). Despite the clear political and economic implications, hospitals that currently use value-based models encounter problems with the economic realities of patients.

Moreover, hospitals with value-based models depend on the strategies of large employers for reducing healthcare costs in patients while having to align patient markets with what physicians have the authority to practice (Tabish & Syed, 2015). Developments in infrastructure and governance have important implications for developing a theory of quality management that considers links between financial investments that supplement revenues lost from patients who cannot pay for health services.

Some of these implications are resource-based in terms of providing ambulatory service and telemedicine while other implications are technology-based with reference to software development and pharmaceutical research (Tabish & Syed, 2015). Operational inefficiencies caused by a staffing shortage and poorly managed supply chains provide the greatest barrier to effective healthcare delivery for ED patients. Along with staffing shortages, poorly managed supply chains provide unnecessary services that lead to significant waste (Tabish & Syed, 2015). Future research on operational efficiencies and poorly managed supply chains should provide substantial opportunities for linking the problem of ED overcrowding with predicting future trends in healthcare delivery.

CHAPTER 5

Discussions, Implications, and Recommendations

Summary of Major Themes in the Literature Review

The purpose of this doctoral dissertation was to examine the interactions between staff and patients in the emergency department (ED) at Detroit Medical Center (DMC) hospital locations. Negative health outcomes that result from ED overcrowding aided in formulating the problem statement that helped identify its causes. Although previous studies paid close attention to identifying the causes of ED overcrowding at DMC hospitals, the problem remains. Evidence of ED overcrowding at DMC hospitals points to extended times in the waiting room lasting more than four hours. A recent economic decline in the Detroit city limits contributed further to the problem of ED overcrowding as many low-income patients with little or no health insurance coverage use these facilities as a primary means of accessing healthcare. Because of continued ED overcrowding, a mixed methods approach was useful for finding solutions to this problem.

Major themes identified in the literature review highlighted the causes of ED overcrowding, infrequent events, access to primary care facilities, clinical health outcomes, quality assurance (QI) and its associated strategies, and financial implications. Causes of ED overcrowding were multiple, though not always related. Input, throughput, and output measures reflect sources of patient flow and bottlenecks within and outside of an ED (Hoot & Aronsky, 2008). Overcrowding is a problem because of how it leads to negative health outcomes including death. With respect to infrequent events like natural disasters and widespread influenza outbreaks, the causes of ED overcrowding are inadequate staffing and bed shortages (Blom et al., 2014; Guttman et al., 2011; Hoot & Aronsky, 2008). These causes reflect an inability to deliver adequate care because of an increased frequency of non-urgent patients who use an ED as a primary source for receiving medical attention.

Other causes of ED overcrowding point to further problems in the triage process where patients arriving at an ED receive an assigned number according to the severity of their illness or injury. Patients without a primary source of care may not receive proper medical attention because of ED overcrowding. Hospital staff reported that having a primary source for receiving care reduces costs and improves the overall quality of delivering healthcare services.

Unfortunately, despite the fact that patients with less severe conditions can schedule ED visits ahead of time, they are now always aware that this type of service is available. In this context, patients and hospital staff perceive some patients as abusers of an entire healthcare system.

The theme of clinical health outcomes among patients points to differences in the quality of care that patients receive depending on the severity of their illness or injury. With respect to wait times, some patients who wait for more than four hours fall under the category of "left without being seen" (LWBS) or "leave against medical advice" (LAMA). These patients ultimately have more adverse health outcomes because of how ED staff must use their time to fill out paperwork explaining why they left without going through the triage process. A suggestion for decreasing wait times included close monitoring of triage systems and promoting an increased availability for patients to access and receive consultations with specialists.

For quality improvement (QI) measures and strategies, taking steps to ensure improvements involved an internal and external analysis. Unfortunately, ED staff at most hospitals have not fully caught on to developing measures and strategies that specifically address structural issues, evaluations of health outcomes, and documentation processes in delivering care. QI measures and strategies ensure that businesses maintain an effective competitive advantage at the organizational level as each industry develops its own measures for improving the quality of products and services provided to customers. QI aims to improve the quality of care that patients receive while working to change the organizational culture.

Measuring quality in the healthcare industry includes the use of data elements that describe individual aspects that patients would consider important. In emergency medicine, providing patients with comfort and reassurance that they will leave the hospital with improved health outcomes is another critical factor for measuring quality in the healthcare system. Three types of quality—clinical, service, and cost efficiency—pointed to barriers of ED staff lacking commitment for improving the organizational culture. Although improving the quality of healthcare delivery for patients may involve the use of innovations in information technology (IT), factors of accountability and transparency are important for ensuring that QI measures and strategies having lasting and effective results.

Benchmarking processes are of further importance for ensuring that QI strategies work effectively. Firmly establishing measures for a maximum ED wait time of four hours was important for this study because of how QI strategies may expedite the triage process. By using information and communications technologies (ICTs), ED staff applies QI measures and strategies to create platforms for identifying potential causes of patient overcrowding (Bhatnagar, 2014). Real-time tracking measures, for example, improve efficiencies in patient flows during the triage process so that some patients are on a fast track to see a physician while others with less severe conditions may actually benefit from waiting longer. Effective QI strategies also worth noting include decreasing ambulance diversion, increasing the number of holding units for waiting patients, improving turnaround times of laboratory work, handling elective surgery caseloads more smoothly, and implementing regional agreements for patient delivery via ambulance.

Lean thinking principles have a strong relation with benchmarking tools and real-time tracking measures for decreasing wait times to a maximum of four hours. For DMC hospitals, lean thinking may aid hospitals in decreasing the number of LWBS and LAMA patients.

However, lean thinking principles may not always guarantee an improvement of health outcomes in patients. While patient flow may improve under lean thinking principles, overall satisfaction with the type of care received during the triage process and during consultation, sessions with a physician are more qualitative variables. Lean thinking principles often involve the use of Six Sigma methodologies with rigidly formalized measures for assessing, improving, and sustaining positive health outcomes of ED patients. Qualitative factors of overall patient satisfaction do not fall under the rigorous and standardized processes of using lean thinking principles in conjunction with a Six Sigma methodology.

The financial implications of using QI measures and strategies for reducing the effects of ED overcrowding and for improving health outcomes in patients are clear. While legislative measures at the state and federal levels affect overall healthcare costs in patients, they may only have a small effect on improving health outcomes. Some states may choose to opt out of paying for medical expenses in patients who use an ED as a source of accessing primary care. As a result, different geographical regions have different measures for assessing the quality of care that ED patients receive. For this study, however, identifying QI measures for improving the quality of care ED patients receive at DMC hospitals revolve around patient-centeredness, timeliness, efficiency, effectiveness, and equity. Because DMC hospitals are in a major metropolitan area, the use of ICTs involved the use of mobile/cellular platforms, alert systems to warn ED staff of possible overcrowding, and real-time coordination across various units within a single hospital. By not implementing the most appropriate QI measures and strategies, DMC hospitals risk running a major financial burden of increasing their operating costs having to administer expensive treatments.

Summary of Methodology

As noted, a mixed methods approach was useful for answering the research questions of how to improve the current state of ED overcrowding at DMC hospitals and of how to improve the health outcomes of patients who must wait more than six hours to receive care. Both quantitative and qualitative measures were used to analyze ED overcrowding that led to an analysis of the sample population selected to participate in this study. Especially in the health sciences, mixed methods research promotes diversity in applications of research findings. Issues in public health have historical links with the problem of ED overcrowding because of how hospitals and social contexts vary from setting to setting over time. Yet, despite the growth of interest in mixed methods research, developing the guidelines for "best practices" in health sciences lead to outdated recommendations that harken back to using Six Sigma methodologies.

By using mixed methods research, this study drew insights from qualitative applications of in-depth interviews, field observations, and case study analysis as found in the social sciences. The qualitative methods used in this study referred to a combination of clinical trials, surveys of attitudes and beliefs among ED staff, and epidemiological research to understand the range of problems occurring within a healthcare organization. Qualitative methods also helped with identifying key processes as they emerged from the data to provide detailed information about the setting and context. Alternatively, this study also used quantitative methods to product deductive analyses of hard data by testing theories and hypotheses derived from descriptive information. Quantitative methods allowed for an examination of the relationships occurring among variables, though they often rely on statistical data to analyze key findings.

The methodologies used in this study contributed to research in QI measures and strategies in the healthcare industry by selecting the sites, population, and sample that informs data collection methods. Methods in QI measures and strategies for improving the delivery of healthcare services at DMC hospitals have a strong relation with best practices research that works to integrate multiple frameworks into a broad theoretical explanation. Methodologies that focus on developing strong QI measures and strategies studies from evaluation research that analyzed the quality of programs implemented to improve overall quality of operations at the organizational level. However, this study mainly drew from formative evaluations. Formative evaluations assisted in pointing out specific areas within DMC hospitals that experienced ED overcrowding. Formative evaluations provided context for answering the two research questions by highlighting the internal and external causal factors of accessing primary healthcare services and health insurance for patients admitted into an ED at DMC hospitals.

In this study, the main hypothesis was that decreased access to primary healthcare services and decreased levels of health insurance availability in the Detroit metropolitan area had a direct relation with ED overcrowding. The null hypothesis was that decreased access to primary healthcare services and decreased levels of health insurance availability bared little or no effect on the status of ED overcrowding. Both the main and null hypothesis referred to the need for researchers to create and implement benchmarking tools for reducing the ED wait times to a maximum of four hours. The hypotheses also pertained to the need for researchers to address the health outcomes of ED patients who wait for more than six hours. Using mixed methods research to test these hypotheses provided internal validity with respect to the findings.

Qualitative methods employed phenomenological research for interview participants via in-depth focus groups for data collection purposes. Phenomenological research aimed to describe the lived experiences of participants to understand how they develop and apply a theoretical framework to their profession. The purpose of using phenomenological research was for participants to engage in a period of self-reflection, also known as *epoché* that strove to identity the core processes behind the problem of ED overcrowding. Using in-depth focus groups, this study aimed to understanding differences in attitudes and beliefs as they are constructed in social and professional environments. In-depth focus groups also helped to provide face validity because of its widespread use as a qualitative research method.

Quantitative methods gained insights from information found in three electronic healthcare databases: the Greater Detroit Area Health Council (GHADC), the Michigan Department of Community Health (MDCH), and Modern Healthcare, a national reporting firm. The GDAHC supplied data for patients using an ED as a primary source for receiving healthcare services at DMC hospitals. Whereas the MDCH provided a database of patients enrolled in Medicare who are also Michigan residents, Modern Healthcare provided a database of trends in health insurance markets of the Detroit metropolitan area and the entire state of Michigan.

Internal data from Modern Healthcare assisted in analyzing uncommon/infrequent events, incident reporting forms, rates of infection, length of ED wait time, frequency of lengthy ED wait times, expenditure reports, boarding time, and complaints from patients. Moreover, data from Modern Healthcare provided tools for conducting an external analysis of patient demographics including race and ethnicity, socioeconomic status, frequency of hospital stays, mortality rates, morbidity linked to risk factors, and treatment procedures. By using these three databases, quantitative measures aided in developing hypotheses based on observations from large data sets, predicting outcomes, collecting data, and verifying measurements and findings. Information contained within each of the three databases aided in developing a correlational design that attempted to determine the degree of relationships between patients and access to primary care, availability of health insurance, and lengthy ED wait times.

Analyzing the data obtained from in-depth interviews with focus group participants aimed to synthesize the principles contained in mixed methods research. The use of nominal, original, interval, and ratio measurements in quantitative research methods were helpful in identifying the frequencies at which participants fell into clearly defined categories. Statistical measures were useful for identifying a central tendency in the findings for DMC hospitals with patients who use an ED as a primary source of receiving medical attention. Any statistical data that did not support the main hypothesis ultimately supported the null hypothesis. Here, the central tendency demonstrated much less variability in the null hypothesis than in the main hypothesis after considering the mean, median, and mode of statistical models found in each of the three databases. With respect to the reliability of the findings in this study, proving that the main hypothesis was consistent and reliable across a wide number of studies helped inform the construction of theoretical propositions that highlighted a correlation regular access to primary care, level of health insurance coverage as applicable, and ED overcrowding. Examining the relationships between the probabilities that a claim is true involved the development of a theoretically informed drawn from an applied understanding of QI measures and strategies.

Discussion of Results

The background and rational of this study indicated that the problem of ED overcrowding throughout the last 25 years is a significant research topic for the health sciences and for the medical community. As the amount of research grows, the number of links pointing to the causes of this problem also grows. Though earlier studies identified, input measures of non- urgent patients using an ED as a primary source for receiving healthcare, measures. In terms of inadequate ED staffing, and output measures referring the shortage of hospital beds, studies that are more recent have highlighted the cause of ED overcrowding as a reflection of a much broader set of problems regarding the efficient delivery of services within the American healthcare system.

Based on the use of in-depth interviews with focus group participants, responses from ED staff members at DMC hospitals with a sufficient knowledge of emergency medicine aided in an application of Kotter's 8-Step Model for implementing system-wide changes (Hickman & Ojo, 2013). Along with the use of focus groups, surveys from participating ED staff members pointed to themes of working in a "successful" professional environment. Related to this theme was the emphasis on reducing "service pressures" that hinder the ability of ED staff to reduce overcrowding. The results indicated that a successful ED does not confront the problem of overcrowding on a frequent basis. However, service pressures may still point to clues on how DMC hospitals can improve their resource capacity. Services pressures may lead to decreased efficiency and effectiveness in delivering care to patients.

Along with the use of Kotter's 8-Step Model, this study applied the PRECEDE/PROCEED Model to analyze perceptions and behaviors regarding predispositions among ED staff about how patients should receive care. The PRECEDE/PROCEED Model provided further assistance for applying the findings to understanding how a successful ED with few service pressures—and, conversely, an unsuccessful ED with significant service pressures— reinforces and rewards professional behaviors among staff at DMC hospitals (Leonard et al., 2012). Moreover, applications of clinical microsystems using the HSE and Stufflebeam/CIPP change models identified the need for greater flexibility in making small changes at the organizational level (O'Dwyer, 2014).

Regarding the first research question that explored relationships between ED overcrowding and adverse health outcomes, survey results indicated that staff at DMC hospitals had poor perceptions about the amount of time that patients spend in triage before seeing a doctor. Patients reported poor service quality when receiving ambulatory care, though survey results indicated an average quality of service as patients waited to transfer into a treatment area. Survey results further indicated an average score of quality regarding three specific aspects: the average length of waiting time in an ED, comfort of the waiting area, and the likelihood that patients will recommend the same ED at a DMC hospital to others.

Through the use of a sentence completion exercise, focus group participants identified perceptions about the outcomes, results, functions, and features of a "successful" ED. Sentence completion exercises provided further assistance for ED staff to identify the types of outcomes that they should avoid. The results of sentence completion exercises indicated that nearly 43 percent of ED staff who participated in this study described a successful ED as not filled with admitted patients, medical patients, and intensive care unit (ICU) patients. A successful ED does not promote a stressful, pressured, or fast-paced environment, though some participants indicated that a successful ED should not act as a referral or holding unit for patients with longer-term medical issues. At the same time, focus group participants indicated that a successful ED should not function as a safety net for patients without primary sources for accessing healthcare services. As for patients waiting in triage, survey results indicated that the use of an Emergency Severity Index (ESI), despite its commonplace status, can contribute to ED overcrowding.

Assigning an ESI number may pose difficulties in facilitating improvement in triage systems. Inconsistent usage of triage systems further contributes to the problem of ED overcrowding because some staff do not have enough professional experience for developing a strong level of confidence. Maintaining confidence in a triage system involves continued training efforts that also require support from documentation when ED staff cannot indicate the reasons for assigning or not assigning a number to patients. Documentation systems in the triage process help with improving both the accuracy of patient information and their overall health outcomes. A general implication to make from the suggested use of documentation systems is that they lead to a more uniform triage process.

Eliminating waste at the front end of an ED can also help reduce overcrowding as staff members at all levels, including security guards, have access to patient records that allow for more efficient and effective delivery of care. Another implication to make from this result is that clear channels of communication are important for finding solutions to the problem of ED overcrowding at DMC hospitals. Training on how to communicate patient information clearly and accurately will help staff at all levels recognize where they work towards making small improvement as problems appear.

Directions for Future Research

The results of this study pointed to the possible use of an All Hazards approach.

Applications of an All Hazards approach suggest that hospitals should institute plans and actions at the organizational level to diverse patient scenarios for reducing the risk that patients may have more adverse health outcomes. While known alternatively as "citizen preparedness," an All Hazards approach can work in conjunction with Lean Management principles for promoting greater efficiency. When combined, the two approaches to addressing the problem of ED overcrowding may also promote improvements in psychological and social welfare. At the organizational level, the implications of combining an All Hazards approach with Lean Management principles are that ED staff will have improved confidence levels of knowing how to improve patient flow during the triage process.

Educational interventions ED staff are especially useful for addressing the medical needs of patients who have no other source of primary care. Many of these patients are from low- income neighborhoods, and that may demonstrate signs of at-risk behaviors associated with intimate partner violence (IPV) and substance abuse. Considering that, the Detroit metropolitan area has a racially diverse population, training interventions for ED staff to recognize how some populations are at a higher risk for developing cardiovascular disease is critical. As observed in the results, participants suggested that efforts for improving throughput measures to address capacity issues at DMC hospitals have wider social and political implications for an entire healthcare system. System-wide improvements at the organizational level for DMC hospitals have even further implications for financial and resource-based recommendations. Therefore, future research in the two areas of improving throughput measures for other hospitals in the US and promoting system-wide improvement for throughput measures is strongly recommended.

For the second research question, improving health outcomes in patients would involve training health professionals on how to better manage multiple time lines, create a stronger organizational vision, and build coalitions with professionals working in different departments of a hospital.

A succinct summation of Kotter's 8-Step Model leads to implications for future research that addresses the need for ED staff at DMC hospitals to establish a sense of urgency while forming strong coalitions. Future research would also need to emphasize how the combination of an All Hazards approach with Lean Management principles leads to the creation and communication of a unified organizational vision can help empower others to act accordingly. Future research can also benefit from analyzing how different stages of Kotter's 8-Step Model works more fittingly in a variety of emergency medical situations. Planning and creating short- term successes may lead to consolidating improvements that promote continued change for institutionalizing new approaches at the organizational level. The implication is that hospitals may need to address specific steps of Kotter's model more closely than others to see fix the problems of ED overcrowding and improve health outcomes of patients.

Contribution of the Study

This study contributes to the existing literature on change models used for solving the problem of ED overcrowding and for improving the health outcomes of patients. Conceptual and theoretical links with Transtheoretical Models (TTMs) may help when applied to future studies by investigating the level of awareness among ED staff about the severity of an illness or injury. TTMs also investigate how patients decide whether they will participate and remain in treatment for their conditions. Studies in quality management may further benefit from explorations of the barriers and facilitators that provide care to patients. Contributions to studies in quality management involve addressing perceptions among ED staff about the training they receive to handle emergency medical situations while they also address perceptions among patients who use an ED to receive care.

With respect to using an ED for reasons requiring psychiatric interventions, unlikely events like natural disasters or a sudden influenza outbreak contribute to studies on the use of ICTs. Data leverage in ICTs is critical for providing accurate information during other events such as a terrorist attack. Future studies on the use of social media platforms by medical professionals may provide a fitting context when addressing an urgent situation requiring medical attention. For DMC hospitals, social media platforms may help ED staff with how they use strategies and approaches to assist public safety officers during unlikely events.

In theoretical terms, strengthening QI measures and strategies at DMC hospitals will need to involve health professionals learning how they can develop strong practical applications that combine personal and professional experience. Because the future of healthcare delivery systems depends on how patients perceive the quality of care, that doctors and nurses provide, the use of data-driven methods may seem more fitting to ensure accuracy and completeness of information from patients arriving at an ED for a wide number of reasons. Adapting to these methods, however, needs to quicken its pace. Infrastructure and governance at the organizational level will continue to have political and economic implications for hospitals that determine the well-being of patients with medical emergencies. As a final recommendation, future research on how hospitals can better manage their supply of available resources for ensuring the delivery of quality healthcare will need to address possible improvements in operational efficiencies.

References

ACEP Medical Legal Committee. (2013, January). *A risk management program for emer- gency medicine; basic components and considerations.* Irving, TX: American College of Emergency Physicians. Retrieved from http://www.acep.org/workarea/downloadasset.aspx?id=90838

Afilalo, J. M., Marinovich, A., Afilalo, M., Colacone, A., Léger, R, Unger, B., & Giguère, C. (2004). Nonurgent emergency department patient characteristics and barriers to primary care. *Academic Emergency Medicine, 11(12)*, 1302-1310. doi: 10.1197/j.aem.2004.08.032

Andersson, G., & Karlberg, I. (2001). Lack of integration, and seasonal variations in demand explained performance problems and waiting times for patients at emergency departments: a 3 years evaluation of the shift of responsibility between primary and secondary care by closure of two acute hospitals. *Health Policy, 55(3)*, 187-207. doi: 10.1016/S0168-8510(00)00113-5

Athanasakis, E. (2013). Synthesizing knowledge about nursing shift handovers: Overview and reflections from evidence-based literature. *International Journal of Caring Sciences, 6(3)*, 300-313. Retrieved from http://internationaljournalofcaringsciences.org/docs/2.%20Athanasakis.pdfd

Atzema, C. L., Schull, M. J., Kurdyak, P., Menezes, N. M., Wilton, A. S., Vermeulan, M. J., & Austin, P. C. (2012). Wait times in the emergency department for patients with mental illness. *Canadian Medical Association Journal, 184*(18), E969-E976. doi: 10.1503/cmaj.111043

Bair, A. E., Song, W. T., Chen, Y., & Morris, B. A. (2010). The impact of inpatient boarding on ED efficiency: A discrete-event simulation study. *Journal of Medical Systems,34*(5), 919-929. doi: 10.1007/s10916-009-9307-4

Bardsley, M., Steventon, A., Smith, J., & Dixon, J. (2013, June). *Evaluating integrated and community-based care.* London: Nuttfield Trust. Retrieved from http://nuffield.dh.bytemark.co.uk/sites/files/nuffield/publication/evaluation_summary_fin al.pdf

Becker, N. V., & Friedman, A. B. (2014). ED, heal thyself. *The American Journal of Emergency Medicine, 32*(2), 175-177. doi: 10.1016/j.ajem.2013.11.002

Begley, C. E., Behan, P., & Seo, M. (2010). Who uses hospital emergency rooms?: Evidence from Houston/Harris County, Texas. *Journal of Health Care for the Poor and Underserved, 21*(2), 606-616. doi: 10.1353/hpu.0.0312

Bergs, J., Verelst, S., Gillet, J., Deboutte, P., Vandoren, C., & Vandijck, D. (2014). The number of patients simultaneously present at the emergency department as an indicator of unsafe waiting times: A receiver operated curve-based evaluation. *International Emergency Nursing, 22*(4), 185-189. doi: 10.1016/j.ienj.2014.01.002

Bernstein, S. L., Aronsky, D., Duseja, R., Epstein, S., Handel, D., Hwang, U., Society for Academic Emergency Medicine, Emergency Department Crowding Task Force (2009). The effect of emergency department crowding on clinically oriented outcomes. *Academic Emergency Medicine, 16*(1), 1-10. doi: 10.1111/j.1553-2712.2008.00295.x

Bernstein, S. L., Verghese, V., Leung, W., Lunney, A., & Perez, I. (2003). Development and validation of a new index to measure emergency department crowding. *Academic Emergency Medicine, 10*(9), 938-942. doi: 10.1197/S1069-6563(03)00311-7

Bhatnagar, S. (2014, March). *Public service delivery: Role of information and communication technology in improving governance and development impact* (ADB Economics Working Paper No. 391). Manila, The Philippines: Asian Development Bank. Retrieved from http://digitalcommons.ilr.cornell.edu/cgi/viewcontent.cgi?article=1368&context=intl

Blom, M. C., Jonsson, F., Landin-Olsson, M., & Ivarsson, K. (2014). The probability of patients being admitted from the emergency department is negatively correlated to in- hospital bed occupancy: A registry study. *International Journal of Emergency Medicine, 7*(1), 1-7. doi:10.1186/1865-1380-7-8

Boudreaux, E. D., Cruz, B. L., & Baumann, B. M. (2006). The use of performance improvement methods to enhance emergency department patient satisfaction in the United States: A critical review of the literature and suggestions for future research. *Academic Emergency Medicine, 13*(7), 795-802. doi: 10.1197/j.aem.2006.01.031

Brown, L. E., Burton, R., Hixon, B., Kakade, M., Bhagalia, P., Vick, C, Hawn, M. T. (2011). Factors influencing emergency department preference for access to healthcare. *Western Journal of Emergency Medicine, 13*(5), 410-415. doi: 10.5811/westjem.2011.11.6820

Bukhari, H., Albazli, K., Almaslmani, S., Attiah, A. Bukhary, E., Najjar, F., Eldin, A. S. (2014). Analysis of waiting time in emergency department at al-Noor Specialist Hospital, Makkah, Saudi Arabia. *Open Journal of Emergency Medicine, 2*(04), 67-73. doi: 10.4236/ojem.2014.24012

Burstin, H. R., Conn, A., Setnik, G., Rucker, D. W., Cleary, P. D., O'Neil, A. C., Brennan, T. A. (1999). Benchmarking and quality improvement: The Harvard emergency department quality study. *The American Journal of Medicine, 107*(5), 437-449. doi: 10.1016/S0002-9343(99)00269-7

Carron, P., Yerson, B., Trueb, L., Gonin, P., & Hugli, O. (2014). Missed opportunities: Evolution of patients leaving without being seen or against medical advice during a six- year period in a Swiss tertiary hospital emergency department. *BioMed Research International, 2014*, n.p. doi: 10.1155/2014/690368

Cassa, C. A., Chunara, R., Mandl, K., & Brownstein, J. S. (2013). Twitter as a sentinel in emergency situation lessons from the Boston Marathon explosion. *PLOS Currents, 5*, n.p. doi: 10.1371/currents.dis.ad70cd1c8bc585e9470046cde334ee4b

Centers for Medicare & Medicaid Services. (2014, July 23). *Emergency medical treatment and active labor act (EMTALA)*. Retrieved from http://www.cms.gov/Regulations-and- Guidance/Legislation/EMTALA/index.html?redirect=/EMTALA/

Chan, H. Y., Lo, S. M., Lee, L. L. Y., Lo, W. Y. L., Yu, W. C., Wu, Y. F., Chan, J. T. S. (2014). Lean techniques for the improvement of patients' flow in emergency department. *World Journal of Emergency Medicine, 5*(1), 24-28. doi: 10.5847/wjem.j.issn.1920-8642.2014.01.004

Cheng, I. L., Lee, J., Mittmann, N., Tyberg, J., Ramagnano, S., Kiss, A., Zwarenstein, M. (2013). Implementing wait-time reductions under Ontario government benchmarks (pay-for-results): A cluster randomized trial of the effect of a physician-nurse supplementary triage assistance team (MDRNSTAT) on emergency department patient wait times. *BMC Emergency Medicine, 13*(1), 1-10. doi:10.1186/1471-227X-13-17

Creswell, J. W., Klassen, A.C., Clark, V. L. P., & Smith, K. C. (2011). Best *practices for mixed methods research in the health sciences.* Bethesda, MD: Office of Behavioral and Social Sciences Research. Retrieved from https://tigger.uic.edu/jaddams/college/business_office/Research/Best_Practices_for_Mi xed_Methods_Research.pdf

Crilly, J. L., Keijzers, G. B., Tippett, V. C., O'Dwyer, J. A., Wallis, M. C., Lind, J. F., … Shiels, S. (2014). Expanding emergency department capacity: A multisite study. *Australian Health Review, 38*(3), 278-287. doi: 10.1071/AH13085 Davidoff, F., Dixon-Woods, M., Leviton, L., & Michie, S. (2015). Demystifying theory and its use in improvement. *BMJ Quality & Safety, 0,* 1-11. doi: 10.1136/bmjqs-2014-003627

Delgado, M. K., Meng, L. J., Mercer, M. P., Pines, J. M., Owens, D. K., & Zaric, G. S. (2013). Reducing ambulance diversion at the hospital and regional levels: Systemic review of insights from simulation models. *Western Journal of Emergency Medicine, 14*(5), 489- 498. doi: 10.5811/westjem.2013.3.12788

Dent, A. W., Phillips, G. A., Chenhall, A. J., & McGregor, L. R. (2003). The heaviest repeat users of an inner city emergency department are not general practice patients. *Emergency Medicine Australasia, 15*(4), 322-329. doi: 10.1046/j.1442- 2026.2003.00470.x

Dickinson, G. (1989). Emergency department overcrowding. *Canadian Medical Association Journal, 140,* 270-271. Retrieved from http://www.ncbi.nlm.nih.gov/pmc/articles/PMC1268622/pdf/cmaj00184-0020.pdf

Ding, R., McCarthy, M. L., Desmond, J. S., Lee, J. S., Aronsky, D., & Zeger, S. L. (2010). Characterizing waiting room time, treatment time, and boarding time in the emergency department using quantile regression. *Academic Emergency Medicine, 17*(8), 813-823. doi: 10.1111/j.1553-2712.2010.00812.x

Donahue, D. A., Cunnion, S. O., Balaban, C. D., & Sochats, K. (2012). All needs approach to emergency response. *Homeland Security Affairs, 8*(1), n.p. Retrieved from http://calhoun.nps.edu/bitstream/handle/10945/24996/124.pdf?sequence=1

Durand, A., Palazzolo, S., Tanti-Hardouin, N., Gerbeaux, P, Sambuc, R., & Gentile. S. (2012). Nonurgent patients in emergency departments: rational or irresponsible consumers? Perceptions of professionals and patients. *BMC Research Notes, 5*(1), 1-9. doi:10.1186/1756-0500-5-525

Finn, J. C., Fatovich, D. M., Arendts, G., Mountain, D., Tohira, H., Williams, T. A., Jabocs, I. G. (2013). Evidence-based paramedic models of care to reduce unnecessary emergency department attendance - feasibility and safety. *BMC Emergency Medicine, 13*(1), 1-6. doi:10.1186/1471-227X-13-13

Francis, R. C., Spies, C. D., & Kerner, T. (2008). Quality management and benchmarking in emergency medicine. *Current Opinion in Anesthesiology, 21*(2), 233-239. doi: 10.1097/ACO.0b013e3282f5d8eb.

Gallagher, E. J., & Lynn, S. G. (1990). The etiology of medical gridlock: Causes of emergency department overcrowding in New York City. *Journal of Emergency Medicine, 8*(6), 785-790. doi: 10.1016/0736-4679(90)90298-A

Greater Detroit Area Health Council, Inc. (2014, January 1). *Report to the community: June 2013—May 2014*. Detroit: Greater Detroit Area Health Council. Retrieved from http://www.gdahc.org/content/gdahc-annual-reports

Gentile, S. Vignally, P., Durand, A., Gainotti, S., Sambuc, R., & Gerbeaux, P. (2010). Nonurgent patients in the emergency department? A French formula to prevent misuse. *BMC Health Services Research, 10*(1), 66-71. doi: 10.1186/1472-6963-10-66

Glaser, C. A., Gilliam, S., Thompson, W. W., Dassey, D. E., Waterman, S. H., Saruwatari, M., ... Fukuda, K. (2002). Medical care capacity for influenza outbreaks, Los Angeles. *Emerging Infectious Diseases, 8*(6), 569-574. doi: 10.3201/eid0806.010370

Gonzalo, J. D., Yang, J. J., Stuckey, H. L., Fischer, C. M., Sanchez, L. D., Herzig, S. J. (2014). Patient care transitions from the emergency department to the medicine ward: evaluation of a standardized electronic sign out tool. *International Journal for Quality in Health Care*, 337-347. doi: 10.1093/intqhc/mzu040

Goralnick, E., Walls, R. M., & Kosowsky, J. M. (2013, September 26). How we revolutionized our emergency department. *Harvard Business Review*. Retrieved from http://blogs.hbr.org/2013/09/how-we-revolutionized-our-emergency- department/

Graff, L., Stevens, C., Spalte, D., & Foody, J. (2002). Measuring and improving quality in emergency medicine. *Academic Emergency Medicine, 9*(11), 1091-1107. doi: 10.1197/aemj.9.11.1091

Green, J., Dawber, J., Masso, M., & Eager, K. (2014). Emergency department waiting times: Do the raw data tell the whole story? *Australian Health Review, 38*(1), 65-69. doi: 10.1071/AH13065

Griffey, R. T., & Bohan, J. S. (2006). Healthcare provider complaints to the emergency department: A preliminary report on a new quality improvement instrument. *Quality and Safety in Health Care, 15*(5), 344-346. doi: 10.1136/qshc.2005.015776

Grouse, A. I., Bishop, R. O., Gerlach, L., de Villecourt, T. L., & Mallows, J. L. (2014). A stream for complex, ambulant patients reduces crowding in an emergency department. *Emergency Medicine Australasia, 26*(2), 164-169. doi: 10.1111/1742- 6723.12204

Grumbach, K., Keane, D., & Bindman, A. (1993). Primary care and public emergency department overcrowding. *American Journal of Public Health, 83*(3), 372-378. doi: 10.2105/AJPH.83.3.372

Guttmann, A. S., Schull, M. J., Vermeulen, M. J., Stukel, T. A. (2011). Association between waiting times and short term mortality and hospital admission after departure from emergency department: Population based cohort study from Ontario, Canada. *British Medical Journal, 342*, d2983-d2983. doi: 10.1136/bmj.d2983

Hearld, L. R., & Alexander J. A. (2012). Patient-centered care and emergency department utilization: A path analysis of the mediating effects of care coordination and delays in care. *Medical Care Research and Review, 69(5)*, 560-580. doi: 10.1177/1077558712453618

Henriksen, D. P., Brabrand, M., & Lassen, A. T. (2014). Prognosis and risk factors for deterioration in patients admitted to a medical emergency department. *PloS One, 9*(4), 1-8. doi: 10.1371/journal.pone.0094649

Hickman, S., & Ojo, O. (2013). Implementing early supported discharge in patients with acute exacerbation of chronic obstructive pulmonary disease. *GSTF International Journal of Nursing and Health Care, 1*(1), 148-159. doi: 10.5176/2345-718X_1.1.20

Hirshon, J. M., Alson, R. L., Blunk, D., Brosnan, D. P., Epstein, S. K., Gardner, A. F., Wheeler, G. (2014). America's emergency care environment: A state-by-state report card. *Annals of Emergency Medicine, 63*(2), 100-243. doi: 10.1016/j.annemergmed.2013.11.024

Holden, R. J. (2011). Lean thinking in emergency departments: A critical review. *Annals of Emergency Medicine, 57(3)*, 265-278. doi: 10.1016/j.annemergmed.2010.08.001

Hong, T. S., Shant, P. P., Arumugam, M., & Yusuff, R. M. (2013). Use of simulation to solve outpatient clinic problems: A review of the literature. *South African Journal of Industrial Engineering, 24*(3), 27-42. Retrieved from http://www.scielo.org.za/scielo.php?pid=S2224-78902013000300004&script=sci_arttext&tlng=pt

Hoot, N. R., & Aronsky, D. (2008). Systematic review of emergency department crowding: Causes, effects, and solutions. *Annals of Emergency Medicine, 52(2)*, 126-136. doi: 10.1016/j.annemergmed.2008.03.014

Houry, D., Hankin, A., Daugherty, J., Smith, L. S., & Kaslow, N. (2011). Effect of a targeted women's health intervention in an inner-city emergency department. *Emergency Medicine International, 2011*, 1-7. doi: 10.1155/2011/543493

Howard, M. S., Davis, B. A., Anderson, C., Cherry, D., Koller, P., & Shelton, D. (2005). Patients' perspective on choosing the emergency department for nonurgent medical care: A qualitative study exploring one reason for overcrowding. *Journal of Emergency Nursing, 31*(5), 429-435. doi: 10.1016/j.jen.2005.06.023

Hung, S., Kung, C., Hung, C., Liu, B., Liu, J., Chew, G., Lee, T. (2014). Determining delayed admission to the intensive care unit for mechanically ventilated patients in the emer gency department. *Critical Care, 18*(4), 485-494. Retrieved from http://www.biomed central.com/content/pdf/s13054-014-0485-1.pdf

Hurwitz, J. E., Lee, J. A., Lopiano, K. K., McKinley, S. A., Keesling, J., & Tyndall, J. A. (2014). A flexible simulation platform to quantify and manage emergency department crowding. *BMC Medical Informatics and Decision Making, 14*(1), 50-60. Retrieved from http://www.biomedcentral.com/content/pdf/1472-6947-14-50.pdf

Hwang, C. E., Lipman, G. S., & Kane, M. (2014). Effect of an emergency department fast track on Press-Ganey Patient Satisfaction Scores. *Western Journal of Emergency Medicine*, in press. doi: 10.5811/westjrm.2014.11.21768

Irvin, C. B., & Atas, J. G. (2007). Management of evacuee surge from a disaster area: Solutions to avoid non-emergent, emergency department visits. *Prehospital Disaster Medicine, 22*(3), 220-223. doi: 10.1017/S1049023X00004702

Jaeker, J. B., Tucker, A. L., & Lee, M. H. (2013, October 24). *Increased speed equals increased wait: The impact of a reduction in emergency department ultrasound order processing time* (Working Paper 14-033). Cambridge, MA: Harvard Business School. Retrieved from http://www.hbs.edu/faculty/Publication%20Files/14-033_cdce77c2-9ffc-4bd4-85f2-b51b3fd7bf44.pdf

Jennings, N., Clifford, S., Fox, A. R., O'Connell, J., & Gardner, G. (2015). The impact of nurse practitioner services on cost, quality of care, satisfaction and waiting times in the emergency department: A systematic review. *International Journal of Nursing Studies, 52*(1), 421-435. doi: 10.1016/j.ijnurstu.2014.07.006

Kang, H., Nembhard, H. B., Rafferty, C., & DeFlitch, C. J. (2014). Patient flow in the emergency department: A classification and analysis of admission process policies. *Annals of Emergency Medicine, 64*(4), 335-342. doi: 10.1016/j.annemergmed.2014.04.011

Kass-Hout, T. A., Xu, Z., McMurray, P., Park, S., Buckeridge, D. L., Brownstein, J. S., GroseClose, S. L. (2012). Application of change point analysis to daily influenza-like illness emergency department visits. *Journal of the American Medical Informatics Association, 19*, 1075-1081. doi: 10.1135/amiajnl-2011-000793

Kellermann, A. L., & Weinick, R. M. (2012, June 7). Emergency departments, Medicaid costs, and access to primary care—Understanding the link. *New England Journal of Medicine 366*(23), 2141-2143. doi: 10.1056/NEJMp1203247

Lambe, S., Washington, D. L., Fink, A. Laouri, M., Liu, H., Fosse, J. S., Asch, S. M. (2003). Waiting times in California's emergency departments. *Annals of Emergency Medicine, 41*(1), 35-44. doi: 10.1067/mem.2003.2

Leonard, J. C., Scharff, D. P., Koors, V., Lerner, B., Adelgais, K. M., Anders, J., … Jaffe, D. M. (2012). A qualitative assessment of factors that influence emergency medical services partnerships in prehospital research. *Academic Emergency Medicine, 19*(2), 161-173. doi: 10.1111.j.1553-2712.2011.01283.x

Liaw, W., Patterson, S., Rabin, D. L., & Bazemore, A. (2014). The impact of insurance and a usual source of care on emergency department use in the United States. *International Journal of Family Medicine*, 1-5. doi: 10.1155/2014/842847

Lin, D., Patrick, J., & Labeau, F. (2014). Estimating the waiting time of multi-priority emergency patients with downstream blocking. *Health Care Management Science, 17*(1), 88-99. doi: 10.1007/s10729-013-9241-3

Liu, S. W., Hamedani, A. G., Brown, D. F. M., Asplin, B., & Camargo, C. A. (2013). Established and novel initiatives to reduce crowding in emergency departments. *Western Journal of Emergency Medicine, 14*(2), 85-89. doi: 10.5811/westjem.2012.11.12171

Lovett, P. B., Kahn, A., Greene, S. E., Bloch, M. A., Brandt, D. R., & Minckler, M. R. (2014). Early quick acuity score provides more complete data on emergency department walkouts. *PloS One, 9*(1), 1-6. doi: 10.1371/journal.pone.0085776

Lowe, R. A., Fu, R., Ong, E. T., McGinnis, P. B., Fagnan, L. J., Vuckovic, N., & Gallia, C. (2009). Community characteristics affecting emergency department use by Medicaid enrollees. *Medical Care, 47*(1), 15-22. doi: 10.1097/MLR.0b013e3181844e1c.

Madsen, T. E., Choo, E. K., Seigel, T. A., Palms, D., & Silver, B. (2015). Lack of gender disparities in emergency department triage of acute stroke patients. *Western Journal of Emergency Medicine, 16*(1), 203-209. doi: 10.5811/westjem.2014.11.23063

Majidi, A., Tabatabaey, A., Motamed, H., Motamedi, M., & Forouzanfar, M. M. (2014). Development of an easy-to-use tool for the assessment of emergency department phy sixal design. *Emergency, 2*(2), 59-65. Retrieved from http://journals.sbmu.ac.ir/emergency/article/download/6061/5192

Marco, C. A., Moskop, J. C., Schears, R. M., Stankus, J. L., Bookman, K. J., Padela, A. I., … Bryant, E. (2012). The ethics of health care reform: Impact on emergency medicine. *Academic Emergency Medicine, 19*(4), 461-468. doi: 10.1111/j.1553- 2712.2012.01313.x

Marmor, Y. N., Golany, B., Israelit, S., & Mandelbaum, A. (2012). Designing patient flow in emergency departments. *IEE Transactions on Healthcare Systems Engineering, 2*(4), 233-247. doi: 10.1080/19488300.2012.736118

Marshall, C., & Rossman, G. B. (2010). *Designing qualitative research.* Thousand Oaks, CA: Sage Publications.

Martens, L., Goode, G. Wold, J. F. H., Beck, L., Martin, G., Perings, C., … Baggerman, L. (2014). Structured syncope care pathways based on lean Six Sigma methodology optimises resources use with shorter time to diagnosis and increased diagnostic yield. *PloS One, 9*(6), n.p. doi: 10.1371/journal. pone.0100208

McCarthy, M. L., Ding, R., Pines, J. M., & Zeger, S. L. (2011). Comparison of methods for measuring crowding and its effects on length of stay in the emergency department. *Academic Emergency Medicine, 18*(12), 1269-1277. doi: 10.1111/j.1553- 2712.2011.01232

McClelland, M. S., Lazar, D., Sears, V., Wilson, M., Siegel, B., & Pines, J. M. (2011). The past, present, and future of urgent matters: Lessons learned from a decade of emergency department flow improvement. *Academic Emergency Medicine, 18*(12), 1392-1399. doi: 10.1111/j.1553- 2712.2011.01229.x

McHugh, M., Van Dyke, K., McClelland, M., & Moss, D. (2011). *Improving patient flow and reducing emergency department crowding* (AHRQ Publication No. 11[12]- 0094). Rockville, MD: U.S. Department of Health and Human Services/Agency for Healthcare Research and Quality.

Mendosa, B. (2009). *Who is using the emergency department for non-urgent care? Characteristics of individuals that use emergency departments as a usual source of care* (Masters thesis). California State University, Sacramento, CA. \

Messina, G., Vencia, F., Mecheroni, S., Dionisi, S., Baragatti, L., & Nante, N. (2015). Factors affecting patient satisfaction with emergency department care: An Italian rural hospital. *Global Journal of Health Science, 7*(4), 30-39. doi: 10.5539/gjhs.v7n4p30

Michigan Department of Community Health. (2014, January 1). Health statistics and reports. *State of Michigan.* Retrieved from http://www.michigan.gov/mdch/0,4612,7-132-2944---,00.html

Morageidge, D., Cai, H., & Jia, J. (2014). Performance-driven design with the support of digital tools: Applying discrete event simulation and space syntax on the design of the emergency department. *Frontiers of Architectural Research, 3*(3), 250-264. doi: 10.1016/j.foar.2014.04.006

Mullan, P. C., Torrey, S. B., Chandra, A., Caruso, N., & Kestler, A. (2014). Reduced overtriage and undertriage with a new triage system in an urban accident and emergency department in Botswana: A cohort study. *Emergency Medicine Journal, 31*(5), 356-360. doi: 10.1136/ ememed-2012-201900

Neuwirth, C., Peck, A., & Simonović, S. P. (2015). Modeling structural change in spatial system dynamics: A Daisyworld example. *Environmental Modelling & Software, 65,* 30- 40. doi: 10.1016/j. envsoft.2014.11.026

Newton, A. S., Rathee, S., Grewal, S., Dow, N., & Rosychuk, R. J. (2014), Children's mental health visits to the emergency department: Factors affecting wait times and length of stay. *Emergency Medicine International, 2014,* n.p. doi: 10.1155/2014/897904

NSW Health Department. (2001). *The clinician's toolkit for improving patient care.* North Sydney, Australia: New South Wales Health Department. Retrieved from www.health.nsw.gov.au/pubs/2001/ pdf/clintoolkit.pdf

Obamiro, J. K. (2013). Effects of waiting time on patient satisfaction: Nigerian hospitals experience. *Journal of Economic Behavior, 3*(1), 117-126. Retrieved from http://ijeb.faa.ro/download/472_7%20 -%20Obamiro.pdf

Oberklaid, F., Barnett, P., Jarman, F., & Sewell, J. (1991). Quality assurance in the emergency room. *Archives of Disease in Childhood, 66*(9), 1093-1098. Retrieved from http://adc.bmj.com/ content/66/9/1093.full.pdf

O'Dwyer, C. (2014). *The introduction of clinical microsystems into an emergency department* (Doctoral dissertation). Royal College of Surgeons in Ireland, Dublin, Ireland. Retrieved from http://epubs. rcsi.ie/cgi/viewcontent.cgi? article=1049&context=mscttheses

Otto, K. (2012, February 29). Do m-health tools really work? Testing the impact of mobile technology on maternal and child health care. *Global Health Hub.* Retrieved from http://www.globalhealthhub. org/2012/02/29/do-m-health-tools-really-work-testing-the- impact-of-mobile-technology-on/

Owad, A. A., Karim, M. A., & Ma, L. (2014). Integrated lean six sigma approach for patient flow improvement in hospital emergency department. *Advanced Materials Research, 834,* 1893-1902. doi: 10.4028/www.scientific.net/AMR.834-836.1893

Pines, J. M., Batt, R. J., Hilton, J. A., & Terwiesch, C. (2011). The financial consequences of lost demand and reducing boarding in hospital emergency departments. *Annals of Emergency Medicine, 58,* 331-340. doi: 10.1016/j.annemergmed.2011.03.004

Pitts, S. R., Carrier, E. R., Rich, E. C., & Kellermann, A. L. (2010). Where Americans get acute care: Increasingly, it's not at their doctor's office. *Health Affairs, 29*(9), 1620-1629. doi: 10.1377/ hlthaff.2009.1026

Rado, O., Lupia, B., Leung, J. M. Y., Kuo, Y., & Graham, C. A. (2014). Using simulation to analyze patient flows in a hospital emergency department in Hong Kong. In A. Matta, J. Li, E. Sahin, E. Lanzarone, & J. Fowler (Eds.), *Proceedings of the International Conference on Health Care Systems Engineering* (pp. 289-301). Milan, Italy: Springer.

Reaves, C. C. (1992). Quantitative research for the behavioral sciences. New York: Wiley and Sons.

Russo, T. (2006). Pandemic planning. *Emergency Medical Services, 35*(10), 51-56. Retrieved from http:// hunt4cleanair.net/Articles/EMSResponderPanFlu.pdf

Rust, G., Ye, J., Baltrus, P., Daniels, E., Adesunloye, B., Fryer, G. E. (2008). Practical barriers to timely primary care access: Impact on adult use of emergency department services. *Archives of Internal Medicine, 168*(15), 1705-1710. doi: 10.1001/archinte.168.15.1705

Sayah, A., Rogers, L., Devarajan, K., Rocker-Kingsley, L., & Lobon, L. F. (2014). Minimizing ED waiting times and improving patient flow and experience of care. *Emergency Medicine International, 2014,* 1-8. doi: 10.1155/2014/981472

Schaaf, M., Funkat, G., Kasck, O., Josten, C., & Winter, A. (2014). \Analysis and prediction of effects of the Manchester Triage System on patient waiting times in an emergency department by means of agent-based simulation. *GMS Medizinische, Biometrie und Epidemiologie, 10*(1), 1-10. doi: 10.3205/ mibe000151

Schull, M. J., Kiss, A., & Szalal, J. (2007). The effect of low-complexity patients on emergency department waiting times. *Annals of Emergency Medicine, 49*(3), 257-264. doi: 10.1016/j.annemergmed.2006.06.027

Schull, M. J., Lazier, K., Vermeulen, M., Mawhinney, S., & Morrison, L. J. (2003). Emergency department contributors to ambulance diversion: A quantitative analysis. *Annals of Emergency Medicine, 41*(4), 467-476. doi: 10.1067/mem.2003.23 Schull, M. J., Mamdani, M. M., & Fang, J. (2004). Community influenza outbreaks and emergency department ambulance diversion. *Annals of Emergency Medicine, 44*(1), 61-67. doi: 10.1016/j.annemergmed.2003.12.008

Singer, A. J., Thode, H. C., Viccellio, P., & Pines, J. M. (2011). The association between length of emergency department boarding and mortality. *Academic Emergency Medicine, 18*(12), 1324-1329. doi: 10.1111/j.1553-2712.2011.01236.x

Skorga, P. Y., & Young, C. F. (2013). Primary care professionals providing non-urgent care in hospital emergency departments. *International Journal of Evidence-based Healthcare, 11*(3), 206-207. doi: 10.1111/1744-1609.12032

Smulowitz, P. B., Lipton, R., Wharam, J. F., Adelman, L., Weiner, S. G., Burke, L., … Landon, B. E. (2011). Emergency department utilization after the implementation of Massachusetts health reform. *Annals of Emergency Medicine, 58*(3), 225-234. doi: 10.1016/j.annemergmed.2011.02.020

Song, Z., Hill, C., Bennet, J., Vavasis, A., & Oriol, N. E. (2013). Mobile clinic in Massachusetts associated with cost savings from lowering blood pressure and emergency department use. *Health Affairs, 32*(1), 36-44. doi: 10.1377/hlthaff.2011.1392

Stone, M., Nguyen, N. D., Moore, J. B., McIntosh, N. P., Jones, M., Zimmerman, J., & Summers, R. L. (2013). Emergency department triage of low acuity patients to a federally qualified health center. *Annals of Emergency Medicine 62*(4), S46-S47. doi: 10.1016/j.annemergmed.2013.07.410

Storm-Versloot, M. N., Vermeulen, H., van Lammeren, N., Luitse, J. S. K., & Goslings, J. C. (2014). Influence of the Manchester triage system on waiting time, treatment time, length of stay and patient satisfaction; a before and after study. *Emergency Medicine Journal, 31*(1), 13-18. doi: 10.1136/emermed-2012-201099

Sun, B. C., Hsia, R. Y., Weiss, R. E., Zingmond, D., Liang, L., Han, W., … Asch, S. M. (2013). Effect of emergency department crowding on outcomes of admitted patients. *Annals of Emergency Medicine, 61*(6), 605-611. doi: 10.1016/j.annemergmed.2012.10.026

Tabish, S. A., & Syed, N. (2015). Future of healthcare delivery: Strategies to reshape the healthcare industry landscape. *International Journal of Science and Research, 4*(2), 727-758. Retrieved from http://www.ijsr.net/archive/v4i2/SUB151330.pdf

Vezyridis, P., & Timmons, S. (2014). National targets, process transformation and local con sequences in an NHS emergency department (ED): A qualitative study. *BMC Emer gency Medicine, 14*(1), 12-22. Retrieved from http://www.biomedcentral.com/content/pdf/1471-227X-14-12.pdf

Victorian Quality Council (VQC). (2008). *A guide to using data for health care quality improvement.* Melbourne: Rural and Regional Health and Aged Care Services Division.

Wang, A. L. (2013, May 13). Emergency room waiting game. *Crain's Chicago Business* Retrieved from http://www.chicagobusiness.com/article/20130511/ISSUE01/305119981/emergency- room-waiting-game

Wang, M., Wild, S., Hilfiker, G., Chmiel, C., Sidler, P., Eichler, K., … Senn, O. (2013). Hospital-integrated general practice: A promising way to manage walk-in patients in emergency departments. *Journal of Evaluation in Clinical Practice, 20*(1), 20-26. doi: 10.1111/jep.12074

Weiss, S. J., Ernst, A. A., & Nick, T. G. (2006). Comparison of the national emergency department overcrowding scale and the emergency department work index for quantifying emergency department crowding. *Academic Emergency Medicine, 13*(5), 513-518. doi: 10.1197/j. aem.2005.12.009

Wells, A. A., Lagomasino, I. T., Palinkas, L. A., Green, J., & Gonzalez, D. (2013). Barriers to depression treatment among low-income, Latino emergency department patients. *Community Mental Health Journal, 49*(4), 412-418. doi: 10.1007/s10597-012 9547-5

Whitfield, C. B. (2013). *Emergency department triage acuity ratings: Embedding ESI into the electronic medical record* (Doctoral dissertation). University of South Carolina, Columbia, SC. Retrieved from http://scholarcommons.sc.edu/cgi/viewcontent.cgi? article=3489&context=etd

Woods, R. W., Reintjes, S., & Nagy, P. (2014). Quality improvement projects based in the emergency department. *Journal of the American College of Radiology, 11(4)*, 423-424. doi: 10.1016/j. jacr.2014.01.0

Zade, A. T., Khob, A. T., Ghomi, Z. K., Panahi, M., & Amini, M. (2014). Impact of using appointment system on patients' satisfaction. *HealthMED: Journal of Society for Development in New Net Environment in B&H, 8*(8), 1007-1012. Retrieved from http://www.healthmed.ba/pdf/healthmed_8_8_web.pdf#page=68

CPSIA information can be obtained
at www.ICGtesting.com
Printed in the USA
LVHW061209290922
729418LV00011B/448